TEST YOUR ENGLISH

TEST
YOUR ENGLISH

BY

D. PENN, B.A.(Hons.)
C. O'HAGAN, M.A.
R. L. MALONE, B.A.(Hons.)

LONDON
MACMILLAN & CO LTD
1963

First published 1962
Reprinted 1963

MACMILLAN AND COMPANY LIMITED
St Martin's Street London WC 2
also Bombay Calcutta Madras Melbourne

THE MACMILLAN COMPANY OF CANADA LIMITED
Toronto

ST MARTIN'S PRESS INC
New York

PRINTED IN GREAT BRITAIN

PREFACE

THESE test-papers in formal English are designed for use in the final year of the normal Primary School course. They provide varied practice in the types of question set in the qualifying examination for entrance to the Secondary School. Since they test all the essentials of language-work covered in the Primary School, they could profitably be used as the basis for a revision course in the first year of the Secondary School.

Although the book has been written in response to specific requests for help from teachers of children whose mother tongue is other than English, it should prove equally useful for English-speaking children preparing for an entrance examination.

There are twelve test-papers, each containing ten questions. The Scheme of Work shows an ordered plan illustrating every aspect of language-work at this level; from the selection and idiomatic use of individual words and phrases to complex sentences exemplifying structure, usage and idiom.

The correct forms of written English are thoroughly tested but a great deal of attention has been paid to natural spoken English, and this emphasis on the living form of language — SPEECH — is deliberate. It is intended to counteract pedantic stilted expression, too often encouraged by a purely academic approach.

These papers both TEST and TEACH. Single exercises or a whole test-paper may be given under examination conditions. Alternatively the book may be used as a self-help manual, the child studying privately, helped by the explanations and examples at the head of each exercise. To give the child a clear idea of what is required, model answers are given side by side with the questions in the first three papers. Answers to subsequent papers will be found at the back of the book.

Most examinations at this level include a paper on Comprehension. The authors have therefore prepared a companion volume *Test Your Understanding of English*. In this again, the aim is not merely to *test* the child's general understanding of a given passage but to *teach* him how to set about reading for information.

LANGUAGE-WORK TESTED

	Test-Paper I	*Test-Paper II*
Verbs	Question-forms	Simple Past tense
Nouns	Association	Formation of Adjectives from
Adjectives	Superlatives	Vague v. Precise
Adverbs	Formation	Position
Prepositions	Choice of correct	Phrasal verbs
Sentences }	Phrasal verbs	Synthesis
	Alternative expression	Synthesis
Analogy	Parts of the body	Gender
Additional } topics	Punctuation	'Y' and 'IES'
	Rhyming words	Indirect Speech

	Test-Paper III	*Test-Paper IV*
Verbs	Passive and Active	Sequence of tenses
Nouns	Formation from Adjectives	Classification
Adjectives	Possessive	Nationality
Adverbs	Use of appropriate	Formation from Adjectives
Prepositions	Inference	Correction of errors
Sentences }	Rearranging confused words	True or False
	Sequence of ideas	Compound
Analogy	Miscellaneous	Miscellaneous
Additional } topics	Articles (Def. & Indef.)	Question-forms
	Negative forms	Spelling

	Test-Paper V	*Test-Paper VI*
Verbs	Correct tense or form	Ending in '-ATE'
Nouns	Odd Man Out	Gender
Adjectives	Opposites	Followed by Prepositions

TEST-PAPER I

Question 1. Change the following statements into questions:

1. Tom can ride a bicycle.
2. He's very ill. (He is)
3. She's sent for the doctor. (She has)
4. They were walking home when it began to rain.
5. She does her homework regularly.
6. Thieves broke into the house last night.
7. That man has some oranges for sale.
8. He cannot swim very far.
9. The doctors did what they could for the injured man.
10. He lay down under the tree and went to sleep.

Answer 1

1. Can Tom ride a bicycle?
2. Is he very ill?
3. Has she sent for the doctor?
4. Were they walking home when it began to rain?
5. Does she do her homework regularly?
6. Did thieves break into the house last night?
7. Has that man (got) any oranges for sale?
8. Can't he (Can he not) swim very far?
9. Did the doctors do what they could for the injured man?
10. Did he lie down under the tree and go to sleep?

Question 2. In the following list of nouns there are five names of articles of furniture, five of buildings, and five of living things. The other five words do not belong to any of these three groups. Make a list of each of the three groups.

armchair; bank; bookcase; cloud; cub; cupboard; desk; diamond; frog; hotel; house; lake; lioness; lizard; prison; school; snow; table; vulture; water.

Answer 2

FURNITURE	BUILDINGS	LIVING THINGS
armchair	bank	cub
bookcase	hotel	frog
cupboard	house	lioness
desk	prison	lizard
table	school	vulture

Question 3. Change the words in brackets so that the sentences make sense:

1. Which is the (tall) building in New York?
2. Father bought John the (big) ball he could find in the shop.
3. Number 7 is the (simple) sum in the exercise.
4. Who is the (good) of the good writers in the class?
5. Mary is the (old) of three sisters.
6. The (busy) street in London is Regent Street.
7. That was the (bad) journey I have ever made.
8. This is the (comfortable) bed I have ever slept in.
9. July was the (wet) month in the whole of 1960.
10. Jane has 60 cts.; Tom has 30 cts.; Mary has 90 cts. Who has the (much) money?

Answer 3

1. tallest	6. busiest
2. biggest	7. worst
3. simplest	8. most comfortable
4. best	9. wettest
5. eldest	10. most

Question 4. Make adverbs from the following (e.g. *politely* from *polite*):

quiet	whole
good	anger
fast	heart
beautiful	repeat
lazy	cruelty

Answer 4. The required adverbs are:

quietly	wholly
well	angrily
fast	heartily
beautifully	repeatedly
lazily	cruelly

Question 5. The words in bold type (Prepositions) in these ten sentences are not the ones we ought to use in English. Write down the ten correct words.

1. John was eating his supper all **to** himself.
2. Six comes **before** five and seven.
3. Pour the boiling water **in** the tea-pot.
4. Do you live **at** England?
5. My nose is **among** my two eyes.
6. He rested his elbows **on to** the table.
7. I am going **for** London by air.
8. We shall not be **to** school tomorrow morning.

9. I haven't received any letters **off** my brother.
10. He knocked the nails in **by** a hammer.

Answer 5

1. by	6. on
2. between	7. to
3. into	8. at/in
4. in	9. from
5. between	10. with

Question 6. In modern English some very common verbs convey different meanings through the addition of prepositions or adverbs. Here are two examples of such *phrasal verbs* with some of their additions:

LOOK: look at; look for; look on; look into; look back; look out for; look up to; look forward to; look back upon.

PUT: put down; put up; put in; put on; put away; put back; put off; put forward; put up with.

In the following exercise match the phrasal verb (in bold type) in each sentence with one of the meanings in the list given below:

1. Do you **go away** during the holidays?
2. Let the guide **go ahead** and we'll follow.
3. During a sale prices **go down**.
4. Do not tease that dog or it may **go for** you.
5. Dogs usually **go after** cats.
6. Guns sometimes **go off** by accident.
7. My brother plays tennis well and **goes in for** every tournament.
8. He also **goes in for** stamp-collecting.
9. The wounded soldier is **going through** a lot of pain.
10. He was determined to **go through with** his plan.

List of Meanings: competes in (enters for); chase; attack; lead; makes a hobby of; are reduced; continue with (carry out); leave this place; explode (are fired); enduring (suffering).

Answer 6

1. leave this place	6. explode (are fired)
2. lead	7. competes in (enters for)
3. are reduced	8. makes a hobby of
4. attack	9. enduring (suffering)
5. chase	10. continue with (carry out)

Question 7.   Alter these sentences by following the instructions given.   Change the sentences as little as possible and try to keep the meaning the same.

1. He was punished because he had broken the law.   (Put 'Because' first)
2. After he had fed the animals, the farmer had his own supper.   (Begin: 'The farmer . . .')
3. He gave me a book.   (Put the word 'me' last)
4. I am strong but I can't lift this box.   (Begin: 'Although I . . .')
5. This box is too heavy for me to lift.   (Begin: 'This box is so heavy . . .')
6. I have always been present.   (Begin: 'I have never . . .')
7. Father, I cannot tell a lie.   (Use part of the verb 'to be unable')
8. He managed to kill the snake.   (Begin: 'He succeeded . . .')
9. I advised him to see a doctor.   (Begin: 'I suggested . . .')
10. I want you to help me with my work.   (Begin: 'Please will . . .')

Answer 7

1. Because he had broken the law he was punished.
2. The farmer had his own supper after he had fed the animals.
3. He gave a book to me.
4. Although I am strong, I can't lift this box.
5. This box is so heavy that I can't lift it.
6. I have never been absent.
7. Father, I am unable to tell a lie.
8. He succeeded in killing the snake.
9. I suggested that he should see a doctor.
10. Please will you help me with my work?

Question 8.   Complete the following.

PARTS OF THE BODY

1. Foot is to —— as hand is to arm.
2. Knee is to leg as —— is to arm.
3. —— is to foot as finger is to hand.
4. Wrist is to arm as —— is to leg.
5. Blind is to eyes as deaf is to ——.
6. Palm is to hand as —— is to foot.
7. Claw is to cat as —— is to human being.
8. Taste is to tongue as —— is to ear.
9. Beard is to chin as moustache is to ——.
10. Child is to children as —— is to feet.

Answer 8

1. leg
2. elbow
3. toe
4. ankle
5. ears
6. sole
7. nail
8. hearing
9. (upper) lip
10. foot

Question 9.   There are two errors in punctuation in each of the
following sentences.   Write the five sentences correctly.

1. Did mary do her homework last night
2. My father is flying to india next week
3. What a pity he couldnt come
4. 'Will you come in said the witch.
5. My mother who lives in Bombay sent me a post-card.

Answer 9

1. Did Mary do her homework last night?
2. My father is flying to India next week.
3. What a pity he couldn't come!
4. 'Will you come in?' said the witch.
5. My mother, who lives in Bombay, sent me a post-card.

Question 10.   In these twenty words there are five sets of
rhyming words (four words in each set).   Write down the
five sets.

bread; fade; fed; feel; fill; head; heel; hill; played;
raid; said; stale; steal; still; vale; veil; wail;
weighed; wheel; will

Answer 10

bread	fade	feel	fill	stale
fed	played	heel	hill	veil
head	raid	steal	still	vale
said	weighed	wheel	will	wail

B

TEST-PAPER   II

Question 1.   Answer these ten questions in full sentences beginning with *Yes.* Use the Simple Past tense and make any other necessary changes.

For example:

> Did he answer your question correctly?
> Yes, he **answered my** question correctly.

1. Did they laugh at you?
2. Did they spend all their wages?
3. Did you see the lions in the Zoo?
4. Did the children eat their breakfast?
5. Did the policeman blow his whistle?
6. Did the teacher teach well?
7. Did you wake up early yesterday?
8. Did the baker bring the bread?
9. Did they swim across the river?
10. Did you find the books you lost?

Answer 1

1. Yes, they **laughed** at **me** (us).
2. Yes, they **spent** all their wages.
3. Yes, **I** (**we**) **saw** the lions in the Zoo.
4. Yes, the children **ate** their breakfast.
5. Yes, the policeman **blew** his whistle.
6. Yes, the teacher **taught** well.
7. Yes, **I** (**we**) **woke up** early yesterday.
8. Yes, the baker **brought** the bread.
9. Yes, they **swam** across the river.
10. Yes, **I** (**we**) **found** the books **I** (**we**) **lost.**

Question 2.   Corresponding to the noun *truth*, we have the adjectives *true* or *truthful*.   Write down one adjective corresponding to each of the following nouns:

anger	peace
height	laziness
breadth	circle
heaven	charm
speed	war

Answer 2

angry	peaceful
high	lazy
broad	circular
heavenly	charming
speedy	warlike

Question 3.   Replace the ten vague words in bold type in the following sentences by more precise or vivid words taken from this list:

tasty; polite; bitter; untruthful; friendly; rotten; beautiful; punctual; exciting; disobedient.

Use each word once only.

1. This medicine has a very **nasty** taste.
2. This apple is too **bad** to cook.
3. Peter tells lies. He is **naughty.**
4. Mary talks to everyone. She is very **nice.**
5. John never does what he is told. He is a **bad** boy.
6. Ruth is a **good** girl. She always says 'Please' and 'Thank you'.
7. My mother gave me a **nice** blue dress for my birthday.
8. Sarah is always late for school but her brother is always **good.**
9. We had a very **nice** curry for dinner.
10. That cowboy film was **good,** wasn't it?

Answer 3

1. bitter
2. rotten
3. untruthful
4. friendly
5. disobedient
6. polite
7. beautiful
8. punctual
9. tasty
10. exciting

Question 4. In the following sentences the adverbs or adverbial phrases in bold type would be better placed elsewhere. Re-write the sentences, putting the words or phrases in bold type where you think they should go.

1. We come **every morning** to school at eight o'clock.
2. She comes **often** to see me in the evenings.
3. I **every day** go to see my uncle.
4. The boy **at last** lost his temper completely.
5. We **soon** shall know if this is a good film.
6. We must **during the holidays** go to see Mr. Smith.
7. My dog waits **always** for me at the gate.
8. I **only** have two pencils on me and one is broken.
9. He needs a hair-cut **badly.**
10. I have **somewhere or other** read that bats are blind.

Answer 4. In some of these sentences there are alternative acceptable answers. The most natural solutions are given.

1. We come to school at eight o'clock every morning.
2. She often comes to see me in the evenings.
3. I go to see my uncle every day.
4. At last the boy lost his temper completely.
5. We shall soon know if this is a good film.
6. During the holidays we must go to see Mr. Smith.
7. My dog always waits for me at the gate.
8. I have only two pencils on me and one is broken.
9. He badly needs a hair-cut.
10. Somewhere or other I have read that bats are blind.

Question 5. Explain the meaning of the words in bold type in the following sentences.

1. My mother has just had influenza but she's **getting over** it now.
2. Jane has bought a new hat. It **goes with** her blue dress.
3. Mary **got through** her examination last May.
4. The lazy boy didn't **take in** a single word of the lesson.
5. An apostrophe often **stands for** a missing letter.
6. We've **run out of** sugar. Please go and buy some more.
7. Last night my aunt left for London. We went **to see her off** at the station.
8. The train **got in** at midnight.
9. My uncle is **looking into** the possibility of buying a house in Spain.
10. He **turned down** the job because the salary was not high enough.

Answer 5

1. recovering from
2. matches
3. passed
4. understand
5. replaces
6. used up all our
7. to say goodbye to her
8. arrived.
9. examining
10. refused

Question 6. Join these ten pairs of sentences together. Write ten new sentences using the words in brackets and making as few changes as possible.

1. This is the house. Jack built it. (that)
2. Yesterday I met my uncle. He had just arrived from America. (who)

3. I bought a large map. It was very useful to me on my walking-tour. (which)
4. It was raining at eight o'clock. At eight o'clock I set out for school. (when)
5. This is the address. I wrote to it. (to which)
6. Shaw was born in Ireland. His plays are known all over the world. (whose)
7. This is the house. I was born in it. (in which OR where)
8. I am very pleased with this pen-knife. Harry gave it to me. (which)
9. My pen-friend is coming to stay with me. I have been writing to him for two years. (to whom)
10. He spent his holidays in Zanzibar. He saw many clove-plantations. (where)

Answer 6.

1. This is the house that Jack built.
2. Yesterday I met my uncle who had just arrived from America.
3. I bought a large map which was very useful to me on my walking-tour.
4. It was raining at eight o'clock when I set out for school.
5. This is the address to which I wrote (which I wrote to).
6. Shaw, whose plays are known all over the world, was born in Ireland.
7. This is the house in which I was born (where I was born, which I was born in).
8. I am very pleased with this pen-knife which Harry gave me.
9. My pen-friend, to whom I have been writing (whom I have been writing to) for two years, is coming to stay with me.
10. He spent his holidays in Zanzibar where he saw many clove-plantations.

Question 7.   Join together each of these ten pairs of sentences to make ten single sentences.   Use the words in brackets and make any other necessary changes.

1. Tom is clever. Tom is selfish. (but)
2. I was dangerously ill. They took me to hospital. (because)
3. She is very old. She still works hard. (although)
4. I know how to do this sum. It is very difficult. (Begin with 'although')
5. I cannot do this sum. It is very difficult. (too)
6. You won't listen to me. I shan't tell you what really happened. (since)
7. We enjoyed our picnic. The rain was heavy. (in spite of)
8. My brother didn't go to the cinema. I didn't go to the cinema either. (neither . . . nor)
9. I am revisiting this country. My last visit was in 1950. (since)
10. I am revisiting this country. My last visit was in 1950. (years ago)

Answer 7.   The following answers are suggested:

1. Tom is clever but selfish.
2. They took me to hospital because I was dangerously ill.
3. Although she is very old, she still works hard.
4. Although this sum is very difficult, I know how to do it.
5. This sum is too difficult for me to do.
6. Since you won't listen to me I shan't tell you what really happened.
7. We enjoyed our picnic in spite of the heavy rain.
8. Neither my brother nor I went to the cinema.
9. This is my first visit to this country since 1950.
10. My last visit to this country was thirteen years ago.

Question 8. Complete the following:

GENDER

1. Father is to mother as brother is to ——.
2. Nephew is to —— as uncle is to aunt.
3. —— is to wife as grandson is to granddaughter.
4. Brother-in-law is to —— as boy is to girl.
5. Male is to female as —— is to feminine.
6. King is to queen as prince is to ——.
7. Duke is to —— as lord is to lady.
8. Actor is to actress as —— is to bride.
9. Mr. is to —— as he is to she.
10. Stepfather is to stepmother as great-uncle is to ——.

Answer 8

1. sister
2. niece
3. husband
4. sister-in-law
5. masculine

6. princess
7. duchess
8. bridegroom
9. Mrs.
10. great-aunt

Question 9

A. Many *singular* nouns end in -*y*. There are two general rules for forming the plurals of such nouns:

1. when the -*y* follows a vowel, add -*s*.
   e.g. *day* (singular); *days* (plural)
2. when the -*y* follows a consonant, change the -*y* into *ies*.
   e.g. *lady* (singular); *ladies* (plural)

Use these two simple rules in order to form the plurals of the following singular nouns:

1. journey 2. country 3. toy 4. key 5. party 6. ray
7. story 8. storey 9. enemy 10. alloy

B. Many *plural* verbs end in *-y*. The third person singular is normally formed according to the two rules given above. e.g.

   1. *They pray*; *he prays* (simply add *-s* if the *-y* follows a vowel)

   2. *They cry*; *she cries* (change *-y* to *ies* if the *-y* follows a consonant)

Use these rules to form the third person singular of the following verbs (Use *He* or *She* before the verb in each answer):

1. stay 2. annoy 3. hurry 4. pity 5. buy 6. deny 7. obey
8. pay 9. reply 10. try

Answer 9

A. 1. journeys 2. countries 3. toys 4. keys 5. parties
   6. rays 7. stories 8. storeys 9. enemies 10. alloys

B. 1. He stays. 2. He annoys. 3. He hurries. 4. He pities.
   5. He buys. 6. She denies. 7. She obeys. 8. She pays.
   9. She replies. 10. She tries.

Question 10

A. Read these five sentences and write down what you think were the actual words spoken. Begin with the words in brackets.

   1. He asked Mary to sit down and wait. ('Please . . .')
   2. She said her father had had an accident. ('My . . .')
   3. He asked me if I would go with him. ('Will . . .')
   4. My brother told me that he couldn't hear what I was saying. ('I . . .')
   5. John explained that he was late for school because he had had a puncture. ('I . . .')

B. Change the following from the form of Direct Speech to that of Indirect Speech.

For example:

> *He said 'I am sorry.'*
> becomes *He said that he was sorry.*

1. 'Stand up at once!' the magistrate ordered the prisoner.
2. I said to my friend 'I'll see you on Friday.'
3. Mary said to me 'I saw your mother on the bus.'
4. 'Can you come to my party?' Peter asked me.
5. The teacher asked John 'Do you know how to do this sum?'

Answer 10

A. 1. 'Please sit down and wait, Mary.'
   2. 'My father has had an accident.'
   3. 'Will you come with me?'
   4. 'I can't hear what you are saying.'
   5. 'I'm late for school because I('ve) had a puncture.'

B. 1. The magistrate ordered the prisoner to stand up at once.
   2. I told my friend that I would see him on Friday.
   3. Mary told me that she had seen my mother on the bus.
   4. Peter asked me if I could go to his party.
   5. The teacher asked John if he knew how to do the sum.

TEST-PAPER III

Question 1. Change the verbs in bold type in these sentences from Active to Passive, making any other changes necessary to complete the sense.

For example:

'*Somebody* is mending *my watch*.'
becomes   '*My watch* is being mended.'

1. The hunter **killed** the lion.
2. The lion **killed** the hunter.
3. Somebody **has stolen** my watch.
4. Bernard Shaw **wrote** this play.
5. They **grow** oranges in California.
6. Somebody **has said** that cheats never prosper.
7. Someone **asked** this question in the House of Commons.
8. They **will open** the gates of the football-ground at two o'clock.
9. They **lock** the school doors every afternoon at five o'clock.
10. They told me somebody **had broken** into their house.

Answer 1

1. The lion was killed by the hunter.
2. The hunter was killed by the lion.
3. My watch has been stolen.
4. This play was written by Bernard Shaw.
5. Oranges are grown in California.
6. It has been said that cheats never prosper.
7. This question was asked in the House of Commons.
8. The gates of the football-ground will be opened at two o'clock.
9. The school doors are locked every afternoon at five o'clock.
10. They told me their house had been broken into.

Question 2.   We say that a person who is *patient* possesses the virtue or quality of *patience*.   What qualities or defects do these people possess?   Write ten words only.

1. A person who is kind.
2. —————— beautiful.

3. A person who is generous.
4. ———————— cowardly.
5. ———————— brave.
6. ———————— humble.
7. ———————— proud.
8. ———————— honest.
9. ———————— wise.
10. ———————— stupid.

Answer 2

1. kindness
2. beauty
3. generosity
4. cowardice
5. bravery
6. humility
7. pride
8. honesty
9. wisdom
10. stupidity

Question 3. Change the words in brackets so that the following sentences make sense:

1. Henry and Mary left for school after saying goodbye to (they) mother.
2. What have you done with (you) luggage?
3. I have forgotten my pen. Will you lend me (you)?
4. Those are our toys; they aren't yours but (we).
5. The parcel was damaged but (it) contents were safe.
6. Mary's dress and my dress are both new but (she) is much smarter than mine.
7. On (she) return Margaret could not find her key.
8. John wanted to borrow (I) book because he had left his at home.
9. Just look at my desk! Yours is tidy but (I) is untidy.
10. Our neighbours have a beautiful house. Ours is smaller than (they).

Answer 3

1. their	6. hers
2. your	7. her
3. yours	8. my
4. ours	9. mine
5. its	10. theirs

Question 4. Choose the most suitable word (from the list given below) to fill the blanks in these sentences. Use each word once only.

1. The monkey —— stuffed the banana into its mouth.
2. 'What a lovely dress!' Jane cried ——.
3. Go and wash your hands. Dinner is —— ready.
4. He walked home very —— because his ankle was hurting.
5. He spoke rather —— because he had a sore throat.
6. Examine your change —— before you leave the shop.
7. Bills should always be paid ——.
8. 'I can't wait any longer,' said the customer ——.
9. We spoke very —— so as not to waken the baby.
10. The little boy gazed —— at the cream-cakes.

List of words: promptly; slowly; greedily; impatiently; longingly; excitedly; softly; hoarsely; carefully; nearly.

Answer 4

1. greedily	6. carefully
2. excitedly	7. promptly
3. nearly	8. impatiently
4. slowly	9. softly
5. hoarsely	10. longingly

Question 5

A. *Tom, Dick and Harry, in that order, are walking in single file* (i.e. one behind the other). Fill in the blanks in the following sentences:

1. Tom is in front of Dick and Dick is —— Harry.
2. Dick is —— Tom and Harry.
3. Harry is —— both Tom and Dick.

B. *Picture A hangs above picture B and picture B hangs above picture C.* Fill in the blanks in these sentences:

1. B is —— A, but —— C.
2. B is —— A and C.
3. C is —— both A and B.

C. *Mary arrived at 8 a.m. Rose arrived at 9 a.m. Jane arrived at 10 a.m.* Fill in the blanks in these sentences:

1. Rose arrived —— Mary but —— Jane.
2. Jane arrived —— both Rose and Mary.

Answer 5

A. 1. in front of   2. between   3. behind
B. 1. below/under; above   2. between   3. below/under
C. 1. after/later than; before/earlier than   2. after/later than

Question 6. Arrange each of the following groups of words to form a sensible sentence. Begin with the word(s) given in brackets:

1. Hurry up to him I told. (I)
2. This lady with wooden legs will be sold by that table. (THAT)
3. I saw the mountain coming round the corner. (COMING)
4. Too to listen was he angry. (HE)
5. Do read better than he does you? (DOES)

6. Live I know where to want you. (I WANT)
7. Sense will you order the alter and the alter. (ALTER)
8. Know you know that I know that I. (I KNOW)
9. You are pretty going to my maid where? (WHERE)
10. Order to be put in words make certain to have a sense. (WORDS)

Answer 6

1. I told him to hurry up.
2. That table with wooden legs will be sold by this lady.
3. Coming round the corner, I saw the mountain.
4. He was too angry to listen.
5. Does he read better than you do?
6. I want to know where you live.
7. Alter the order and you will alter the sense.
8. I know that you know that I know.
9. Where are you going to, my pretty maid?
10. Words have to be put in a certain order to make sense.

Question 7

Here are two short stories in each of which the sentences are written in the wrong order.
Re-arrange the sentences to make two sensible stories:

A. Peter and Mary fetched some paper and some wood.
'Thank you very much, children' said their mother. 'That's a lovely fire!'
'Come and help me, Peter!' Mary called to her brother.
'Please, Mary, make the fire for me,' said her mother.
They put the wood on top of the paper and Peter lit the fire.

B. 'Yes I like this very much. I'll take this one,' she said.
Mary tried the white dress on and it fitted her perfectly.

Yesterday afternoon Mary went to buy herself a new party dress.

'Here is a very pretty white dress,' said the shop-assistant. While Mary was paying the bill, the assistant packed the dress in a long flat box.

Answer 7

A. 'Please, Mary, make the fire for me,' said her mother.
'Come and help me, Peter,' Mary called to her brother.
Peter and Mary fetched some paper and some wood.
They put the wood on top of the paper and Peter lit the fire.
'Thank you very much, children,' said their mother. 'That's a lovely fire!'

B. Yesterday afternoon Mary went to buy herself a new party dress.
'Here is a very pretty white dress,' said the shop-assistant.
Mary tried the white dress on and it fitted her perfectly.
'Yes I like this very much. I'll take this one,' she said.
While Mary was paying the bill, the assistant packed the dress in a long flat box.

Question 8. Complete the following:

1. Stable is to horse as —— is to dog.
2. Crawl is to snake as swim is to ——.
3. Right is to left as —— is to down.
4. —— is to cow as lamb is to sheep.
5. Bark is to dog as —— is to lion.
6. London is to England as Paris is to ——.
7. —— is to good as worse is to bad.
8. Poor is to poverty as proud is to ——.
9. Patient is to doctor as —— is to teacher.
10. The French are to France as the —— are to China.

Answer 8

1. kennel	6. France
2. fish	7. better
3. up	8. pride
4. calf	9. pupil
5. roar	10. Chinese

Question 9.   Put in *a, an* or *the* to complete the following sentences correctly.

1. These apples cost —— shilling —— pound.
2. The train travelled at sixty miles —— hour.
3. Who discovered —— North Pole? Was he —— American?
4. The greedy boy chose —— biggest apple in the dish.
5. Please pass —— bread.
6. There is —— cat outside the window. It isn't —— one I saw yesterday.
7. The doctor came to the house three times —— day.
8. This has been —— exciting morning.
9. We have only —— small garden but —— Botanical Gardens are quite near.
10. —— unselfish man always tries to help —— poor.

Answer 9

1. a; a	6. a; the
2. an	7. a
3. the; an	8. an
4. the	9. a; the
5. the	10. An; the

Question 10.   Write down the following sentences in an appropriate negative form. If you know more than one suitable answer, write more than one.

1. My brothers can swim.

c

2. All my brothers can swim.
3. She will be present tomorrow.
4. She knows how to play the piano.
5. My friend brought us some sweets.
6. I received some letters this morning.
7. He is either careless or stupid.
8. They came last night, didn't they?
9. I can find something suitable.
10. You understand that, don't you?

Answer 10

1. My brothers can't (cannot) swim.
2. Not all (of) my brothers can swim.
   None of my brothers can swim.
3. She won't (will not) be present tomorrow.
   She will be absent tomorrow.
4. She doesn't (does not) know how to play the piano.
5. My friend didn't (did not) bring us any sweets.
6. I didn't (did not) receive any letters this morning.
   I received no letters this morning.
7. He is neither careless nor stupid.
8. They didn't (did not) come last night, did they?
9. I can't (cannot) find anything suitable.
   I can find nothing suitable.
10. You don't (do not) understand that, do you?

TEST-PAPER IV

(Answers to the questions in Test-Papers IV to XII will be
found at the end of the book beginning on page 73)

Question 1

A. In the following sentences, put the verbs in bold type into
   the Simple Past tense and make any other necessary changes.
   Example:

   Q. He **works** *so hard that he is tired out.*
   A. He **worked** *so hard that he* **was** *tired out.*

   1. He **knows** he has made a mistake.
   2. They **want** to be paid early on Saturday.
   3. He **thinks** he is going to pass.
   4. We **are** sure that it will rain.
   5. I always **do** what I think is right.

B. Change the following into the form of Reported Speech.
   Example:

   Q. He said to us 'I'll see you again at four o'clock.'
   A. He said (told us) that he would see us again at four
       o'clock.

   1. She said 'I'm going home soon.'
   2. She said 'The carpenter can mend it.'
   3. He said to me 'I shall always remember you.'
   4. He said 'A thief stole my purse a few minutes ago.'
   5. I said to her 'I want to see what you have done.'

Question 2.   Here are twenty nouns.   Put them into groups
   under each of these five headings.   (There are four words in
   each group.)

   (*a*) Articles of Clothing
   (*b*) Animals
   (*c*) Metals
   (*d*) Vegetables
   (*e*) Birds

The twenty words are:

belt; blouse; camel; cabbage; crow; gazelle; giraffe; gold; iron; jacket; kite; lead; onion; ostrich; pigeon; potato; puppy; silver; tie; turnip.

Question 3. Fill in the gaps in the following tables:

Britain	British
Egypt	
	Irish
Italy	
	Polish
Portugal	

Germany	German
Spain	
	Dutch
Congo	
	Japanese
Ghana	

Question 4. In the following sentences insert adverbs which correspond to the adjectives given in brackets.

Example:

Q. Jane wrote her name (careful) at the head of the paper.
A. **carefully**

1. Mother waited (anxious) for news from the hospital.
2. My brother always drives too (fast).
3. Dick (foolish) left his books at school.
4. Peter swims very (good), I think.
5. We could hear the church bells ringing (merry).
6. If you work (hard), you will succeed.

7. I can't (possible) do that at present.
8. John stood up (respectful) as the magistrate entered.
9. You are (whole) to blame for this.
10. I missed the bus this morning because I got up too (late).

Question 5. Correct these sentences in which the mistakes are connected with the wrong use of prepositions:

1. My friend is married with a doctor.
2. Is John any good with football?
3. Why is that man staring to us?
4. Your teacher is very satisfied at your progress.
5. Mr. and Mrs. Black left to England from Mombasa last night.
6. The Director of Education congratulated our school for its examination results.
7. People's voices often sound different by the telephone.
8. He isn't interested at anything but cricket.
9. I'm too busy for to do it now.
10. Ask to him if he will help you.

Question 6. Here are ten pairs of sentences. If the two sentences cannot **both** be true at the same time, write *One untrue*. If they **can** both be true at the same time, write *Possible*.

1. All swans are white. Some swans are black.
2. Some dogs have short tails. Some have not.
3. Everybody in my class is over fifteen. One boy in my class is fourteen.
4. Most men are selfish. Some men are selfish.
5. Most men are selfish. Some men are not selfish.
6. Many animals have small ears. Many animals have big ears.

7. Many members of my family enjoy reading. Few members of my family enjoy reading.
8. There are a few cigarettes in my case. There are some cigarettes in my case.
9. Few people have been to Brazil. Most people have been to Brazil.
10. Wordsworth wrote some magnificent poetry. Wordsworth wrote some very bad poetry.

Question 7. Choose the most suitable word (from those in brackets) to join the following pairs of sentences:

1. He was very ill (and; but; so) we called in the doctor.
2. She is clever (so; but; because) she isn't friendly.
3. It is very late (but; so; and) we can still catch the last train.
4. You must go now (and; so; or) you will miss the bus.
5. He is honest (so; because; although) he is stupid.
6. He is very poor (so; but; or) he is perfectly honest.
7. You do it your way (so; and; although) I'll do it mine.
8. His work is interesting (and; but; so) he is badly paid.
9. I feel very lonely (although; because; but) my friend has gone to another school.
10. I've got my umbrella (so; but; because) I don't care if it rains.

Question 8. Complete the following:

1. Third is to fourth as —— is to April.
2. Lion is to roar as —— is to neigh.
3. False is to —— as rude is to polite.
4. Pedal is to —— as handle is to hand.
5. Baby is to baby's as men is to ——.
6. Pineapple is to fruit as cauliflower is to ——.
7. Sweet is to sugar as —— is to lemon.

8. Mutton is to —— as veal is to calf.
9. Waiter is to waitress as —— is to duchess.
10. Mouse is to —— as house is to houses.

Question 9. Give the question-form of the following statements.
Example:

Statement — He went to the cinema last night.
Question-form — Did he go to the cinema last night?

1. She was very clever.
2. He is leaving for London tonight.
3. Pigs can't fly.
4. Tom does his work well.
5. He did up his shoe-lace.
6. His parents bought a large house.
7. His mother gives him pocket-money every week.
8. We must be kind to others.
9. He stole some apples.
10. What you've just said is true.

Question 10. There is one spelling mistake in each of the following sentences. Find it and write the word correctly.

1. The mountain was wraped in cloud.
2. Allthough it was raining, John went for a walk.
3. Prince Charles is a descendent of Queen Victoria.
4. The Principle of our school is Mr. Brown.
5. Please pass me a desert spoon, Mother.
6. We had a marvelous holiday last summer.
7. The theif ran away with my friend's bag.
8. They made there escape through a hole in the roof.
9. The farmer was sewing his corn.
10. The cashier was adding up a long colum of figures.

TEST-PAPER V

Question 1. Correct the tense or the form of the verbs in the following sentences where necessary.

1. After he done his work he went to bed.
2. Last night I seen a very good film.
3. I am working hard since two o'clock.
4. If you are boiling water it turns into steam.
5. You hadn't ought to do that.
6. If it will rain tomorrow, the match will be cancelled.
7. He is wanting to be a doctor.
8. Every one of these mangoes are rotten.
9. Last night, while I have been doing my homework, the doctor came.
10. I can see five birds out of the window. They fly very low.

Question 2.

A. In each of these lines of five words, one word does not fit in suitably with the other four.

Write down the word which you think does not fit.

Example:

   Q. ounce; pound; yard; stone; ton.
   A. yard. (It is a measure of length. The other words are not.)

1. sister; mother; aunt; uncle; daughter.
2. triangle; cube; square; rectangle; hexagon.
3. bellow; roar; neigh; crawl; bleat.
4. puppy; lamb; foal; cub; cow.
5. gold; ruby; silver; copper; aluminium.

B. Now look at the four words you have left in each line. Decide on a title for each group.

Example:

ounce; pound; stone; ton — Units of Weight.

Question 3.   Write down single words contrary in meaning to the adjectives in bold type in the following sentences.

1. He is a very **obedient** little boy.
2. There was a **wide** gap between the hills.
3. These cigarettes are very **cheap.**
4. Apples are **plentiful** this year.
5. This is a very **modern** building.
6. The river is very **deep** at this point.
7. My sister is in one of the **junior** forms.
8. This is a **temporary** solution.
9. These valleys are **barren.**
10. The **minimum** wage is ten pounds a week.

Question 4.   Replace the words in bold type by a single word with the same meaning.

Example:

Q. *'Stop, thief!' he cried* **in a loud voice.**
A. *Loudly*

1. My aunt visits us **at regular intervals.**
2. Do try to behave **in a sensible manner.**
3. Cinderella was dressed **in shabby clothes.**
4. We asked the doctor to come **without any delay.**
5. The floods are subsiding **little by little.**
6. Please contribute **with generosity** to this appeal.
7. The trains in England almost always arrive **at the stated time.**
8. He faced his enemies **with courage.**
9. The tramp shuffled on his way **in a dejected mood.**
10. The flag waved **in triumph** over the conquered city.

Question 5.   Fill in the gaps with suitable prepositions.

1. Cut this apple —— two.

2. We had to send —— the doctor.
3. Our Principal insists —— punctuality.
4. Is your house insured —— fire?
5. We were prevented by a sudden storm —— going to the cinema.
6. There was a heated argument about politics —— John and his brother.
7. Mary has a big part —— the school play.
8. This room is very dusty. Please attend —— it at once.
9. You can always rely —— him for encouragement.
10. For months he suffered —— constant head-aches.

Question 6

A. Look at these two short sentences:

> *He is very poor. He cannot buy any books.*

They have a common subject — *He.* We can join them in this way:

> *He is too poor to buy any books.*

Now join these pairs of sentences in a similar way, using the word 'too'.

1. She was very late. She did not catch the train.
2. He is very old. He cannot work.
3. He is very proud. He does not visit his former friends.
4. She was very lazy. She did not sweep under the chairs.
5. I am very tired. I can't stay up any longer.

B. If the sentences do not have a common subject, we can still join them in *this* way:

    Example:

> *It is very cold. I cannot work outside.*
> *It is too cold* **for me** *to work outside.*

    Now do these in a similar way:

1. It is very wet. We cannot play football.
2. This sum is very difficult. She cannot do it.

3. The box is very heavy. You cannot lift it.
4. It was very late. They could not get a bus home.
5. He spoke very fast. I could not understand what he was saying.

Question 7. Correct these sentences.

1. He asked me what would I like for my birthday.
2. Cinderella was very unhappy, isn't it?
3. Mr. Smith learned us how to make paper aeroplanes.
4. Our hens lay four eggs yesterday.
5. Why you are making such a noise?
6. They left there luggage at the station.
7. She laid down on the grass in the warm sunshine.
8. This pair of scissors are not very sharp.
9. Neither of these two books are very interesting.
10. We had a lesson yesterday about Shakespeare whom, our teacher said, was the greatest English playwright.

Question 8. Complete the following:

1. —— is to cricket as racquet is to tennis.
2. Yes is to —— as positive is to negative.
3. Question is to —— as why is to because.
4. Tomorrow is to today as today is to ——.
5. Pork is to pig as —— is to sheep.
6. Goose is to —— as ox is to oxen.
7. 5 is to number as E is to ——.
8. Early is to late as clean is to ——.
9. Sing is to sang as hear is to ——.
10. Us is to we as —— is to they.

Question 9. There is a mistake (connected with the misuse of a pronoun) in each of the following sentences. Re-write the sentences correctly.

1. Peter and myself hope to see you again soon.
2. That's not your bag. Who's is it?

3. They amused theirselves by playing a new game.
4. May John and me go to the pictures tonight?
5. Look at these two colours and tell me that you prefer.
6. Where is the book what I lent you last week?
7. Father gave my sister and I a shilling each.
8. That dog seems to have hurt it's leg.
9. Between you and I, I'm rather worried about it.
10. Last night I met my uncle from America who I'd never seen before.

Question 10.   In each of the following words underline the syllable which you think should be the **most** strongly stressed (said most emphatically).   For example we say <u>Ca</u>nada but Ca<u>na</u>dian.

1. courage; courageous
2. Italy; Italian
3. relate; relative
4. artist; artistic
5. photograph; photographer
6. regular; regularity
7. electric; electricity
8. metal; metallic
9. accident; accidental
10. mechanic; mechanism

TEST-PAPER VI

Question 1.   Here are fifteen verbs ending in *-ate*:

Celebrate; confiscate; create; debate; dictate; dislocate; educate; elevate; elongate; hesitate; imitate; impersonate; lubricate; narrate; regulate.

Here are the meanings of ten of the verbs listed.   Match these meanings with the appropriate verb.

1. to make longer.
2. to tell (a story).
3. to hold a ceremony in honour of.
4. to hold back in doubt.
5. to bring into existence.
6. to discuss a question.
7. to raise.
8. to displace a joint.
9. to take away property as a punishment.
10. to read out for someone to write down.

Question 2. *Brother* is a masculine noun and *Sister* is the corresponding feminine noun. Fill in these columns:

MASC.	FEM.	MASC.	FEM.
Uncle		tiger	
	women		daughter
King		he	
	witch		grandmother
fox		master	
	cow		female
nephew		god	
	madam		Girl Guide
bachelor		brother-in-law	
	widow		duchess

Question 3.   Fill in the gaps in the following sentences with a suitable preposition.

1. My mother is very fond —— flowers.
2. My brother is keen —— stamp-collecting.
3. Jack is very pleased —— his new bicycle.
4. You should be ashamed —— yourself.
5. We are all sorry —— Mary. She lost her purse.
6. I am tired —— reading.
7. Harry was grateful —— John's help.
8. Never be envious —— other people's good fortune.
9. Who is responsible —— this?
10. Please don't be angry —— him.

Question 4.   In the following sentences the position of adverbs (or adverbial phrases) could be improved. Re-write the sentences making whatever changes you think best.

1. Did you go yesterday there?
2. Foreigners can sometimes write very well English.
3. I have finished just this book.
4. He goes never to bed early.
5. We are for our holidays going to France.
6. We have only lost two matches this season.
7. I must be by seven o'clock at the station tomorrow morning.
8. Before have you been here ever?
9. I have nearly always for breakfast toast.
10. At 11 a.m. the First World War ended in 1918 on November 11th.

Question 5.   In each of the following sentences there is an adverbial phrase of time. Pick out the phrase and write it down using figures.

Example:

> Q. *Can you come to my office before eleven o'clock to-*
> *morrow morning?*
> A. *before 11 a.m. tomorrow*

1. I haven't eaten anything since nine o'clock last night.
2. They're expecting us for dinner at any time from seven o'clock onwards.
3. Surgery hours are from six o'clock to eight every evening except on Sundays.
4. On New Year's Eve, at the stroke of midnight, all the church bells ring.
5. Come to tea between half past four and five on Wednesday.
6. We had breakfast earlier than usual this morning. We had finished by ten past seven.
7. I'll meet you at the Post Office at about a quarter to eight this evening.
8. We begin work at quarter past eight every morning.
9. Yesterday, because of a puncture, I didn't get in till twenty-five to nine.
10. The satellite will be overhead at exactly twenty-three minutes before midnight.

Question 6. Change the phrases in bold type in the following sentences to clauses conveying the same meaning. Begin the clause with the word given in brackets.

Example:

> Q. **On his arrival at the airport,** *he was met by several*
> *reporters.* (*When* . . .)
> A. **When he arrived at the airport,** . . .

1. I don't understand **the meaning of this.** (what . . .)

2. This is a picture showing **the scene of the accident.** (where . . .)

3. **On reaching London,** I went straight to the hotel. (As soon as . . .)

4. I dislike him **on account of his rudeness.** (because . . .)

5. **In spite of his bad cold,** he still went to work. (Although . . .)

6. Do you know **the time of the next bus to Manchester?** (when . . .)

7. Can you describe **your method of making a curry?** (how . . .)

8. He passed his examination **without working very hard.** (although . . .)

9. **As a result of this man's stupidity,** the whole platoon was captured. (Because . . .)

10. Tell me **your reason for not wanting to go.** (why . . .)

Question 7.

A. Change *so* to *such* in the following sentences and make whatever other changes are necessary.

1. He is so rich that he has his own aeroplane.
2. Ireland is so small that it would fit inside Lake Victoria.
3. John was so greedy that he took all the sweets.
4. She is so kind that everybody loves her.
5. They went so fast that we were left behind.

B. Change *such* to *so* and make whatever changes are necessary.

1. He was such a kind man that everybody loved him.
2. Cinderella was such a beautiful girl that the Prince wanted to marry her.
3. You are such a clever student that you will pass the examination easily.

4. My dog is such a fierce animal that we are not afraid of burglars.

5. Yesterday was such a cold day that we couldn't have P.E. outside.

Question 8.   Complete the following:

1. French is to France as —— is to Holland.
2. Three is to —— as two is to bicycle.
3. The lira is to Italy as the —— is to America.
4. Shan't is to shall as —— is to will.
5. Japan is to Tokyo as —— is to Rome.
6. A decade is to ten as a century is to ——.
7. Athens is to Greece as —— is to Germany.
8. A —— is to a week as two is to one.
9. January is to June as thirty-one is to ——.
10. Done is to do as —— is to speak.

Question 9.   The phrases in bold type are quite common in colloquial English.   Re-write the sentences, replacing the phrases by more formal expressions.

Example:

Q. I don't know **the ins and outs** *of the story.*
A. the exact details

1. It's raining **cats and dogs.**
2. I slept **like a log** last night.
3. He stood by his friend **through thick and thin.**
4. You must be **pulling my leg.**
5. My uncle must be **getting on for forty.**
6. I find my old aunt **very trying** at times.
7. Stop **beating about the bush.**
8. Jane is always **hard up** at the end of the month.

D

9. I shouldn't like to be **in your shoes.**
10. Tom was full of mischief. He was always getting **into hot water.**

Question 10. Here is a list of ten proverbs numbered 1–10. Following it is a list (a–j) of simple explanations of the proverbs, but not in the same order. Say which letter corresponds to which number.

1. Birds of a feather flock together.
2. Look before you leap.
3. A little help is worth a deal of pity.
4. Imitation is the sincerest form of flattery.
5. Where there's a will, there's a way.
6. Many hands make light work.
7. One man's meat is another man's poison.
8. Don't count your chickens before they're hatched.
9. Practice makes perfect.
10. Make hay while the sun shines.

a. What suits one person does not necessarily suit another.
b. Work is much more quickly done if everybody concerned helps.
c. People of similar character tend to like each other's company.
d. If a person wants something badly enough, he will find a way of getting it.
e. Consider a situation carefully before going into action.
f. If you persevere in doing something difficult, you will eventually do it well.
g. Make the most of every opportunity as it arises.
h. Practical assistance is more valuable than verbal sympathy.

i. Don't make plans for the future which depend on events that may never happen.

j. What proves that a person is truly respected is that his example is followed by others.

TEST-PAPER VII

Question 1

Read this passage:

Every day after school I come home and do my homework. Then I have my tea. For tea I eat some sandwiches and drink a glass of milk my mother has got ready for me. After tea I go to my father's shop. I sell things to the customers. Whenever they buy anything I write down its name and cost. At six o'clock I begin to clean the shop. I sweep the floor and dust the shelves. At a quarter to seven it grows dark and my father brings me back home in his van.

Re-write the passage beginning with the words 'Yesterday after school I ——' and making all the necessary changes of tense.

Question 2. We talk about a herd of buffaloes. What is the name for a collection or group of:

1. sheep 2. bees 3. hounds 4. ships 5. fish.

Can you think of suitable words to put in these five spaces?

6. a bunch of ——
7. a gang of ——
8. a team of ——

9. a string of ——
10. a clump of ——

Question 3. In each of the following sentences there is an adjective in brackets. Replace it with the correct form of the verb corresponding to the adjective.

Example:

    Q. Please remember to (safe) silver paper for the hospitals.
    A. save

1. Can you (descriptive) what happened in the story?
2. Please let me (full) my pen from your bottle of ink.
3. A good citizen (obedient) the laws of his country.
4. They (wide) the road last week.
5. (Hot) some coffee for me, please.
6. Is your teacher (satisfactory) with your work?
7. Selfish drivers (dangerous) the lives of everybody.
8. I can't (decisive) what to do next.
9. It's impossible to (pleasant) everybody.
10. Are you (enjoyable) your book?

Question 4. Use suitable adverbial *clauses* to complete these sentences.

Example:

    Q. I went straight to bed **after** ——.
    A. after I had finished my homework.

1. They went into the cinema **as soon as** ——.
2. Visitors to the Cathedral are not allowed to wander **wherever** ——.
3. He stared at me **as if** ——.
4. I'm very tired this morning **because** ——.
5. He plays the piano very well **although** ——.
6. Will you say it again slowly **so that** ——.

7. He talked **such** a lot of nonsense **that** ——.
8. You aren't **as** careful **as** ——.
9. **The more** I hear about Italy, **the more** ——.
10. You'll never pass the examination **unless** ——.

Question 5. Change the meaning of these sentences by altering the word(s) in bold type in each. Your new word(s) should be contrary in meaning to the original.
For example:

> *Q. He stepped* **over** *the rope.*
> *A.* **under**

1. I'll meet you just **before** six o'clock.
2. The car went smoothly **up** the steep hill.
3. He got **off** the bus just before it stopped.
4. The average mark was slightly **below** 50.
5. They'll wait for us just **inside** the main gate.
6. Put the milk-bottles **in front of** my desk.
7. Pour the water **into** the jug.
8. He walked slowly **towards** the Post Office.
9. He is a little better now. He can walk **with** a stick.
10. We are all going to the show, **except** Mary.

Question 6. Complete these sentences by means of suitable *clauses*. Begin with the words given in brackets.
Example:

> *Q. We'll go to the football match this afternoon (if . . .)*
> *A. if the car is repaired in time.*

1. (Whenever . . .) I always take a book of detective stories with me.
2. I want to explain to you (that . . .).
3. I haven't seen him (since . . .).
4. (Unless . . .) I shall begin to be worried.

5. He's walking with a limp (as if . . .).
6. This is the young lady (to whom . . .).
7. Will you put all the brushes away (after . . .).
8. It is certainly true (that . . .).
9. (As soon as . . .) he realised that some money was missing.
10. The man (whom . . .) is a great friend of mine.

Question 7. Write questions to which the following would be suitable answers. Each of the ten could, of course, answer many different questions. Choose a question which would be used in natural conversation.

1. About a month.
2. Purple, I think.
3. At nine o'clock.
4. Queen Elizabeth II.
5. A mile and a half.
6. Fifteen.
7. Yes, I do.
8. Two years ago.
9. English.
10. It's over there on the left.

Question 8. Complete the following:

1. A is to Z as first is to ——.
2. Hangar is to —— as garage is to car.
3. Double is to —— as two is to one.
4. Tap is to pat as tub is to ——.
5. A dozen is to a —— as twelve is to twenty.
6. Lion is to lioness as boar is to ——.
7. Widow is to wife as widower is to ——.
8. Beginning is to end as upper is to ——.
9. Advantageous is to advantage as —— is to profit.
10. Went is to go as —— is to put.

Question 9. Punctuate the following passage correctly:

Hello, John!' said Tom 'I was hoping you'd ring me this morning. Its a long time since we've seen you if youre not busy on thursday can you and Mary come round about seven oclock'

'What a pity' answered John. 'We'd have liked to come very much. But Marys brother whom you probably remember has just arrived from Manchester. We cant very well leave him by himself, can we'

'Thats all right. Bring him along too' said Tom. we'll be very glad to see him.

Question 10. Here are ten sets of five words. In each set, pick out the word which does *not* rhyme with the word in capital letters.

1. KEY — tea, they, he, bee.
2. LOVE — dove, stove, above, glove.
3. DEAD — said, bed, bead, bread.
4. ROUGH — tough, plough, stuff, enough.
5. DAY — weigh, quay, obey, prey.
6. EARL — curl, pearl, whirl, real.
7. KNOWN — own, grown, town, sewn.
8. MET — ate, debt, sweat, wheat.
9. PORT — taut, draught, caught, bought.
10. EARTH — worth, forth, berth, birth.

TEST-PAPER VIII

Question 1. Study these two examples carefully:

    A. Mr. Master **showed** *Mr. Servant how to do the work.*

    B. Mr. Master **congratulated** *Mr. Servant on having done the work.*

Notice how the change of verb from *show* to *congratulate* demands other changes in the sentence.

Now complete the following sentences using any appropriate tense in your additions.

1. Mr. Master **wanted** Mr. Servant —— the work.
2. Mr. Master **ordered** Mr. Servant —— the work.
3. Mr. Master **made** Mr. Servant —— the work.
4. Mr. Master **saw** Mr. Servant —— the work.
5. Mr. Master **prevented** Mr. Servant —— the work.
6. Mr. Master **asked** Mr. Servant if —— the work.
7. Mr. Master **hoped** that Mr. Servant —— the work next day.
8. Mr. Master **expected** Mr. Servant —— the work.
9. Mr. Master **thanked** Mr. Servant —— the work.
10. Mr. Master **suggested** that Mr. Servant —— the work next morning.

Question 2. In the word **un**known the *un* at the beginning means *not*. Can you explain the meaning of the parts in bold type in the following words?

1. **bi**cycle
2. **sub**marine
3. **mis**judge
4. **in**human
5. **pre**-war
6. care**less**
7. beauti**ful**
8. simpl**ify**
9. wait**ress**
10. mov**able**

Question 3. Choose suitable words from those given in brackets to complete the following sentences.

1. I haven't much money but I've (a few; enough; much; most) to pay my fare.
2. Mary hasn't (many; any; much; several) books at home. She has only three.
3. Go and buy some more sugar, please. I haven't (some; plenty; a little; any) left.

4. I don't want much sugar in my tea. Just (some; a few; a little; little) please.

5. Most of the boys were here at eight o'clock but (more; most; a few; all) came late.

6. Many people write books but (enough; a little; few; much) write good books.

7. She has very (few; little; enough; much) money but she is very happy.

8. (Several; most; all; some) the children attended the school concert.

9. We saw (all; most; several; plenty) women wearing beautiful hats.

10. A few of these flowers are fresh but (all; few; most; much) of them are dead.

Question 4.   Correct the following sentences:

1. I haven't seen Henry since five years.
2. He isn't enough well to come back to school yet.
3. He worked as hardly as he could.
4. We have lived in Africa during a year.
5. My uncle has been to America two times.
6. That isn't quiet true.
7. During I was waiting at the dentist's, I read a magazine.
8. Because of the traffic I had to drive slowlier than usual.
9. I am rather certain about that.
10. The Governor also came too to our Open Day.

Question 5.   Correct the following sentences.   There are two mistakes (mainly connected with Prepositions) in each sentence.

1. My uncle was born at Bombay but now he lives at England.
2. It takes only ten minutes to get to home on bus.
3. Is anything the matter about you?   You look rather pale for me.

4. My teacher sits to a big desk at the front off the class-room.

5. Don't try to sharpen your pencil by that razor-blade. Ask to Peter to lend you his knife.

6. For my surprise I found Mary sitting with herself in the dark.

7. My father's plane arrived in London Airport at three o'clock at the afternoon.

8. The ball went between the window-pane and knocked a vase of the table.

9. Write the address to this parcel and send it on surface-mail.

10. Your answer is different than Peter's. Go back in your desk and try the sum again.

Question 6.   Re-arrange the words in brackets to make Noun Clauses which will complete these ten sentences.

1. I can't understand (he says what).
2. It all depends on (you mean by what 'easy').
3. Can you tell me (the Bank is where)?
4. The doctor said (measles had my that brother).
5. I don't care (it do whether or you not).
6. He told me (you to him had been how kind).
7. Do you know (he three copies yesterday's ordered why paper of)?
8. The police have not yet discovered (responsible was the accident for who).
9. It's a shame (you my be able that to come party to won't).
10. We don't know for certain (results when will be the examination published).

Question 7

A. Replace the words in bold type in each sentence by one word conveying the same meaning.

1. Many children **come** all the way to school **on foot.**
2. Mary **paid** her father **a visit** when he was in hospital.
3. Tweedledum **had a quarrel** with Tweedledee.
4. In September I intend **to go** to Rome **by air.**
5. The passengers **got off the ship** early on Saturday morning.

B. Explain **in a phrase** the meaning of the words in bold type.

1. Some children **cycle** to school.
2. You will have to **lengthen** the sleeves.
3. I can't **decide** what to do next.
4. Unless you **improve** your writing you'll get a bad report.
5. He **apologised** for his bad behaviour.

Question 8.   Complete the following:

1. Ireland is to island as Spain is to ——.
2. North-East is to —— as eastward is to westward.
3. 1788 is to the —— century as 1988 is to the twentieth.
4. Emigrant is to immigrant as —— is to import.
5. Europe is to —— as Germany is to country.
6. Small is to large as dwarf is to ——.
7. Fish is to —— as bird is to aviary.
8. Feline is to cat as canine is to ——.
9. Tobacconist is to tobacco as florist is to ——.
10. —— are to two as triplets are to three.

Question 9.   Correct the following sentences.   In each there are two errors connected with number (singular and plural).

1. Pigs is sometimes called swines.
2. Several passer-bys were splashed with mud by the Army lorrys.
3. These knifes are not sharp enough to cut breads.
4. I don't know whether I should write 'two spoonfulls of sugar' or 'two spoonsful of sugar'.

5. One of the young ladies were combing her hairs.
6. Don't bother cooking any potatos. We have two loafs of bread to eat up.
7. Young bulls or cows are called calfs, but small cat's are called kittens.
8. The monkies were sitting on the rooves of the huts, eating bananas.
9. The tailor cut out a pair of trouser with his scissor.
10. Those sheeps in the lorry belong to my brother-in-laws.

Question 10

A. In the following sentences, what do you think were the actual words used by the speaker?

1. He said he was sorry that he hadn't been able to come before.
2. The policeman asked the motorist if he had his driving-licence on him.
3. John and Mary asked their mother if they might go for a picnic.
4. Aunt Mary told me that she hadn't had time to ice the cake for my birthday.
5. I told my teacher yesterday that I should have to stay at home today.

B. Change the following from the form of Direct Speech to that of Indirect Speech.

1. 'Do you know why zebras are striped?' my uncle asked me.
2. My grandmother said to my sister Mary, 'I want you to stay with me for the holidays.'
3. 'Be careful not to miss your bus,' my mother said.
4. 'I'll try to do it as soon as I have time', said the workman.
5. 'Has my suit been sent to the cleaners?' Mr. Smith asked his wife.

TEST-PAPER IX

Question 1. The verbs *go* and *say* are words of very general meaning. It is often better to use a more precise or vivid word. Re-write the following sentences, choosing the word which you think most suitable:

1. The cripple **went** slowly along the road. (strolled; ran; limped; marched)
2. 'Somebody must have told you my name!' **said** Rumpelstiltskin angrily. (replied; shrieked; stated; answered)
3. The clouds were **going** like white boats across the blue sky. (crawling; moving; swimming; drifting)
4. 'God bless you, sir,' **said** the toothless old woman. (stated; went on; mumbled; objected)
5. The lizard **went** through a tiny crack in the wall. (sauntered; wriggled; ran; came)
6. 'That is absolutely untrue!' she **said** heatedly. (murmured; mentioned; retorted; uttered)
7. The smoke **went** lazily upwards in the still air. (flew; lifted; curled; rushed)
8. 'You're quite right,' I **said**. (accepted; agreed; spoke; continued)
9. The swan **went** gracefully across the lake. (slid; slipped; glided; rode)
10. 'Please forgive me just this once,' he **said.** (requested; pleaded; asked; demanded)

Question 2

A. Give one word for:

1. a man who sells vegetables and fruit.
2. —————— looks after a building.

3. ———————— sells fresh meat in a shop.
4. ———————— collects the fares on a bus.
5. ———————— writes stories or articles for a newspaper.

B. Now describe the work of the following people: (Do it briefly like this — *A dentist is a man who looks after people's teeth.*)

1. A shepherd
2. A tailor
3. A nurse
4. An architect
5. A blacksmith

Question 3. Add ten different suffixes (endings) to the following words to make them into adjectives. No change is necessary before the addition of the suffix. The adjectives should have the meanings given in brackets.

1. end (without end)
2. wonder (causing wonder)
3. danger (causing danger)
4. green (rather green)
5. friend (willing to make friends)
6. magnet (having the properties of a magnet)
7. eat (that can be eaten)
8. conversation (used in conversation)
9. express (expressing meaning or emotion)
10. second (of less importance)

Question 4. Here is a list of twenty verbs. Choose the most suitable word from the list to replace the words in brackets in the following sentences:

Absolved; approached; approved; assented; deplored; dissolved; implored; inscribed; muttered; prescribed;

reprieved; reproved; resented; resolved; revolved; strode; stroked; strolled; strutted; stuttered.

1. He (made up his mind) to work much harder.
2. She (found fault with) her husband for his extravagance.
3. The lump of sugar slowly (melted) in the warm water.
4. The giant (walked with long swinging strides) towards the door of the castle.
5. As the train (got near to) the level-crossing, the driver blew the whistle.
6. He (felt indignant at) the accusation.
7. The doctor (directed as a medicine) a course of sulphur tablets.
8. The prisoner (begged earnestly) the magistrate to lessen his sentence.
9. The old woman stood in the rain and (spoke indistinctly in a low tone) to herself.
10. The two friends (walked quietly and unhurriedly) through the streets of the town.

Question 5. Choose the correct preposition from those given in brackets.

1. I have not seen him (for; since; during) five years.
2. Ceylon is to the south (by; to; of) India.
3. He arrived (at; in; to) England in 1950.
4. These finger-prints on the window-sill were made (from; with; by) the burglar.
5. Lions were prowling (aside; around; among) our tent all night.
6. The ball sped (among; inside; between) the goal-posts.
7. I am very surprised (at; with; of) what you say.
8. Pour this milk (in; into; inside) the saucer for the cat.
9. She is doing this (at; to; for) your benefit.
10. His hair kept falling (through; along; over) his eyes.

Question 6

A. Study these sentences:

1. If he won a thousand pounds, he would buy a car.
2. If she had worked harder, she would have passed her examination.
3. If the doctor comes, ask him to have a cup of tea.
4. If it hadn't rained yesterday afternoon, we could have played football.
5. If he could have afforded it, he would have gone to the theatre.

Now answer *Yes, No* or *I don't know* to these questions:

1. Did he win a thousand pounds?
2. Did she pass her examination?
3. Did the doctor have a cup of tea?
4. Did it rain yesterday afternoon?
5. Did he go to the theatre?

B. Use the right tense of the verb in brackets:

1. If water (freeze), it turns into ice.
2. If he (listen) to your advice, he would have succeeded.
3. If I (have) a magic ring, I would wish for a lot of money.
4. If she had thought more carefully, she (not do) what she did.
5. If you have been listening carefully, you (be able) to do this exercise by yourself.

Question 7. Make up ten sentences contrary in meaning to those given. In your sentences make use of the words given in brackets.

Example:

Q. Peter's father knows everything about electricity. (*very little*)

A. Peter's father knows very little about electricity.

1. He says he can come. (impossible)
2. I can read your writing easily. (illegible)
3. We couldn't see the mountain at all. (visible)
4. It has rained hard for several days. (not . . . at all)
5. John doesn't go to the cinema very often. (every week)
6. According to the magistrate, the prisoner had committed the crime. (innocent)
7. He didn't believe he would pass the examination. (quite certain)
8. I have never read any of Shaw's plays. (many)
9. All of these apples are green. (None)
10. Few people have heard of the explorer, Livingstone. (very famous)

Question 8. Complete the following:

1. Loud is to loudly as good is to ——.
2. Yard is to length as hour is to ——.
3. Widen is to wide as —— is to long.
4. —— is to two as first is to one.
5. Tuesday is to Monday as —— is to Wednesday.
6. Long is to length as deep is to ——.
7. Written is to writing as —— is to speaking.
8. Never is to always as seldom is to ——.
9. Go is to went as —— is to did.
10. Less is to least as —— is to best.

Question 9. In each of these sentences there is an error connected with the use or misuse or omission of *a, an* or *the*. Rewrite the sentences correctly.

1. He is youngest boy in the class.
2. This is a exercise on Articles.
3. I am studying the Mathematics.
4. He hasn't got an handkerchief.
5. This is a centre of the circle I have just drawn.

E

6. A sideboard is article of furniture.
7. I have never met more generous a man.
8. The more you study, more difficult it becomes.
9. A straight line is a shortest distance between two points.
10. The humility is a rare virtue.

Question 10

A. Here are five negative sentences which might be used in conversation. Rewrite them using the longer form customary in written English.

1. We shan't have finished by September.
2. She won't believe you.
3. He usedn't to behave so strangely.
4. Aren't I right?
5. Don't you understand how to do it?

B. Put these five affirmative sentences into the negative form used in conversation.

1. I saw him yesterday.
2. Do that!
3. He likes reading.
4. She will be able to come.
5. He knew what to do.

TEST-PAPER X

Question 1

A. Make these negative statements into positive questions.
   Example:

> *Q. She hadn't finished her homework.*
> *A. Had she finished her homework?*

1. He hadn't enough money.
2. She won't be able to come.

3. You didn't do your homework last night.
4. They don't know how to do it.
5. We can't get there before six.

B. Now make negative questions from these positive state-ments.

Example:

> Q. *She was wearing a red dress.*
> A. *Wasn't she wearing a red dress?*

1. He knows the answer.
2. He knew the answer.
3. The train left punctually.
4. She saw him last night.
5. He put the money in his pocket.

Question 2. There are many pairs of words in English which are pronounced in the same way as each other but which are spelt differently.

For example:

> (a) *The* **rain** *fell steadily for many hours.*
> (b) *He was born in the* **reign** *of King Henry VIII.*

Now make five pairs of sentences of your own to show that you understand the difference in meaning between these pairs of words:

1. tail; tale
2. flour; flower
3. bough; bow
4. peace; piece
5. profit; prophet

Question 3. The following sentences sound strange because they contain mis-placed words or phrases.

Re-write them correctly with as little change as necessary.

1. Can you see the black dog big?
2. There were tiny blue four flowers on each stem.
3. The teacher drew a thin yellow long line on the blackboard.
4. He is of the two the taller.
5. Pleased I am that you can come.
6. Tired are you after all this work?
7. She grew more beautiful and more as the years went on.
8. I found 'Kidnapped' a story most exciting.
9. In like the present times men are anxious about the future.
10. Shakespeare was the playwright greatest of all time.

Question 4. Here are ten pairs of sentences. Look carefully at each pair. If both the sentences can be true at the same time, write *Possible*. If they cannot both be true at the same time, write *One untrue*.

1. a. Sometimes I enjoy listening to music.
   b. Sometimes I don't enjoy it.
2. a. I always have sugar in my tea.
   b. I don't often have sugar in my tea.
3. a. He came to my house every day last week.
   b. He came to my house only once last week.
4. a. She never wears a hat.
   b. She occasionally wears a hat.
5. a. Usually children like sweets.
   b. Some children don't like sweets.
6. a. Peter frequently goes to the cinema.
   b. He never misses a cowboy film.
7. a. I never listen to plays on the wireless.
   b. I sometimes listen to the news.
8. a. My sister often listens to the news broadcast.
   b. Sometimes she listens to plays.

9. a. It rained most mornings last month.
    b. There was no rain at all last month.
10. a. Sometimes my brother plays chess.
     b. He very seldom plays draughts.

Question 5.   Give the meaning of the words in bold type in the following sentences.

1. We can easily **put you up** for the night.
2. Luckily he had some money **put by** for a rainy day.
3. Are you **looking forward to** the holidays?
4. Men instinctively **look up to** a brave leader.
5. We keep **putting off** our holidays because of the weather.
6. I won't **put up with** his rudeness any longer.
7. Does the new baby **take after** his father or his mother?
8. **Take down** these figures and do the problem yourself.
9. He intends to **go in for** bee-keeping.
10. We'll **go into** this question later.

Question 6

A. Replace the clauses in bold type in the following sentences by phrases which convey a similar meaning. The beginning of a suitable phrase is given in brackets each time.

1. He always took his camera **when he visited the Game Park.** (On his ——)
2. **Although he was frequently interrupted,** he completed the work in three days. (In spite of ——)
3. **He had no sooner arrived at his brother's house than** he fell seriously ill. (Immediately after ——)
4. **I was very surprised that** he refused to see me. (To my ——)
5. **His leg was badly injured so** he could only walk with difficulty. (Because of ——)

B. Replace the phrases in bold type by clauses of similar meaning. Begin with the word in brackets:

1. **In spite of all his efforts,** he could not split the log. (Although ——)
2. **On the receipt of this information** Mr. Churchill was very relieved. (When ——)
3. **Until the invention of the aeroplane** it took six weeks to reach Australia. (Before ——)
4. **Because of his poverty** he often went hungry. (Because ——)
5. **At every possible opportunity,** the R.A.F. pilots bombed the convoy. (Whenever ——)

Question 7

A. In English we sometimes use a simile, likening a person to an animal (or bird or insect) because of some quality apparently common to both. Thus we say a man is *as cunning as a fox.*

Complete the following similes:

1. As —— as a mule.
2. As —— as a peacock.
3. As —— as a bat.
4. As —— as a lion.
5. As —— as a bee.

B. Complete these similes also. They are not connected with animals.

1. As solid as ——.
2. As cold as ——.
3. As sharp as ——.
4. As light as ——.
5. As white as ——.

Question 8. Complete the following.

1. Brownish is to brown as —— is to red.
2. Strong is to strength as broad is to ——.
3. Boy is to boy's as boys is to ——.
4. Theirs is to they as —— is to we.
5. Went is to go as —— is to write.
6. —— is to who as him is to he.
7. This is to that as —— is to there.
8. Shoe is to foot as —— is to hand.
9. There is to —— as then is to when.
10. —— is to begin as loving is to love.

Question 9. Which interrogative word(s) should be inserted in the following questions to which short answers are given in brackets.

1. —— came first in the examination? (Mary did.)
2. —— of these two do you prefer? (That one.)
3. —— did you go for the summer holidays? (To Mombasa.)
4. —— do we use for fixing screws? (A screwdriver.)
5. —— don't we use a hammer for screws? (It would damage them.)
6. —— did you see him last? (On Thursday.)
7. —— is that altogether? (Five shillings, please.)
8. —— sums did you manage to do? (Nine.)
9. —— do you go to the cinema? (About once a week.)
10. —— is your mother? (Very well, thank you.)

Question 10. In this list of thirty words there are ten, and only ten, which are spelt wrongly. Find them and write them down with the correct spelling.

accept	receive	lovable	excellent
parralel	laboratory	dissappointed	cieling
fulfil	deceive	allways	seperate

conveniant	unimportant	physician	lavatory
temperate	necessary	garrage	discipline
machinery	fashion	cruelly	vacinate
engage	changeable	thought	
believe	skillful	medecine	

TEST-PAPER XI

Question 1.   Insert the appropriate Past Participle in the following sentences.

Example:

I ran faster than I have ever **run** *in my life.*

1. Tomorrow I shall see somebody I have never —— before.
2. You can't strike a match again once it has been ——.
3. I ate more than I had ever —— before.
4. We had to write an exercise we had already —— earlier in the term.
5. He sang a song he had not often —— before.
6. You must have —— something you didn't do last time.
7. Have you —— the chickens yet. You must feed them every evening.
8. Drink this! When you've —— it you'll feel better.
9. He hasn't —— his new car yet. Perhaps he's going to buy it tomorrow.
10. The train must have —— by now. It was due to go at three o'clock.

Question 2.   We have many pairs of words in English which are spelt the same, but which we pronounce differently. We pronounce them differently by different stressing (saying one syllable more strongly than another).

So we say:

    a. *Your* **con***duct has been very unsatisfactory lately.*
but b. *A world-famous musician will con***duct** *the orchestra.*

Now look at the words in bold type in the following sentences and write them down like this: 1. a. exports 1. b. export, etc.

Then underline the syllable (in each of the ten words) which you think should be strongly stressed.

1. a. The chief **exports** of Kenya are coffee and sisal.
   b. We **export** some tea as well.
2. a. He was not **content** to remain idle.
   b. The **contents** of the trunk were attacked by white ants.
3. a. This year the school **record** for the mile was broken.
   b. I intend to **record** the rainfall every day in April.
4. a. He said he would not **object** to my doing that.
   b. The **object** he held in his hand was a large knife.
5. a. The **progress** of a country depends on the labour of its people.
   b. In Mathematics we **progress** from simple examples to more difficult.

Question 3. Use suitable adjectives (corresponding to the words given in brackets) to complete the following sentences.
    Example:

      Q. Was it absolutely (necessity) to do that?
      A. necessary

1. John's work is highly (satisfy).
2. I was extremely (gratitude) for his help.
3. We had a very (enjoyment) time at the concert.
4. (Disobey) children are a nuisance to everybody.
5. A mamba is a (poison) snake.
6. I saw a most (amuse) film last night.
7. There was a (moment) pause in the conversation.

8. It is always (advice) to think before you speak.

9. The (skill) surgeon carried out a successful operation.

10. (Care) work is proof of an untidy mind.

Question 4. In each of the following sets of adverbs or adverbial phrases there is one word or phrase which is out of place. Find the 'odd man out'.

Example:

> Q. *Regretfully; excitedly; punctually; angrily. These are all adverbs. But 'punctually' simply means 'keeping to an agreed time' whilst the other three could all describe the feelings of a person doing an action.*
>
> A. *Punctually*

1. Quietly; busily; noisily; loudly.

2. Slowly; hastily; bravely; quickly.

3. At eight o'clock; during the week; at mid-day; at midnight.

4. Sometimes; never; everywhere; always.

5. Visibly; pleasantly; enjoyably; agreeably.

6. In the corner; an hour ago; at the side; on the top.

7. Below; beneath; beside; besides.

8. Forwards; backwards; always; sideways.

9. On Wednesday; in March; last Friday; next Saturday.

10. Immediately; sorrowfully; sadly; gladly.

Question 5. Explain the difference in meaning between the two sentences in each of the following pairs.

1. a. He poured the beer in the cellar.
   b. He poured the beer into the cellar.

2. a. The rabbit ran across the road.
   b. The rabbit ran along the road.

3. a. He took a photograph of his shop-counter.
   b. He took a photograph off his shop-counter.

4. a. Livingstone gave a large sum of money **for** the wretched slave.

   b. Livingstone gave a large sum of money **to** the wretched slave.

5. a. **Because of** what you say, I will do this at once.

   b. **In spite of** what you say, I will do this at once.

Question 6.   Give simple definitions of the following words. Example:

> *An architect is a man who designs buildings.*

1. Auctioneer
2. Author
3. Bachelor
4. Burglar
5. Chauffeur
6. Hermit
7. Pauper
8. Sculptor
9. Teetotaller
10. Warder

Question 7.   Read these two sentences:

   a. *You haven't a handkerchief to lend me,* **have you**?

   b. *You have been listening carefully,* **haven't you**?

The words in bold type are called question-tags.   Add suitable question-tags to the following statements.

1. King Richard was a very brave soldier,
2. You can't change a ten-shilling note for me,
3. You know how to do this question,
4. He hasn't been here today,
5. You'll remember to give them my message,
6. He gave you enough money,
7. You won't forget to bring the bread,
8. They must have left it in the cupboard,
9. It isn't five o'clock yet,
10. He hasn't been feeling very well lately,

Question 8.   Complete the following:

1. Thinking is to thought as seeing is to ——.
2. Deed is to do as —— is to verb.

3. Best is to good as —— is to bad.
4. Circle is to sphere as square is to ——.
5. —— is to lion as puppy is to dog.
6. Arrow is to —— as bullet is to gun.
7. Light is to —— as white is to black.
8. Wings are to bird as —— are to fish.
9. A half is to a quarter as a third is to ——.
10. Do is to don't as —— is to shan't.

Question 9

A. Fill in the gaps in the following table.

I	me	my	mine
You	you		
	him	his	
She	her		
		our	ours
They		their	

B. Which of the twenty-four words in the table would you use to express:
1. You and I
2. them and me
3. you and they
4. belonging to us (Possessive Adjective)
5. belonging to them (Possessive Pronoun)

Question 10. Here are ten questions.
1. Are these yours or hers?
2. Is he seven or eight?

3. Which of these are yours?
4. Has everybody got a blue pencil?
5. Did he lend it to you?
6. Is he seven or is she seven?
7. How many oranges did he buy?
8. Did he give it to your brother?
9. Have you got a red pencil and a blue pencil?
10. Did he buy bananas or oranges?

Here are ten answers. Words in bold type are to be strongly stressed (said emphatically). Study the questions and answers carefully and match each answer with the appropriate question.

a. No, he gave it to **me.**
b. No, he **gave** it to me.
c. **Those** are mine.
d. Those are **mine.**
e. **I** haven't got a blue one yet, Miss.
f. I haven't got a **blue** one yet, Miss.
g. He's **seven.**
h. **He's** seven.
i. He bought **two** oranges.
j. He bought two **oranges.**

TEST-PAPER XII

Question 1. Choose a suitable verb from this list to complete each of the sentences below. Use the correct form of the verb: to patter; to creak; to bang; to beat; to screech; to howl; to rustle; to tick; to crackle; to peal.

1. My alarm clock —— very loudly.
2. Early on Sunday morning all the church bells began to ——.
3. She was wearing a silk dress which —— as she walked.
4. The rain was —— steadily on the tin roof.

5. I couldn't sleep last night because a door kept ——.
6. He threw the dry twigs into the flames and they ——
   fiercely.
7. When hinges ——, oil them.
8. We heard the drums —— far away in the jungle.
9. It was a stormy night and the wind was —— loudly
   through the trees.
10. He jammed his foot down hard and the brakes —— as
    his car came to a sudden stop.

Question 2. Complete the following table:

Singular	Plural	Singular	Plural
day	days	man	men
book		tooth	
box		spoonful	
toy		sheep	
fly		thief	
monkey		knife	
baby		half	
woman		roof	
child		potato	
hand		house	
foot		mouse	

Question 3. In each of these lines of five adjectives one word does not fit in suitably with the other four. Write down the word which you think does not fit.

Example:

> *Q. happy; shabby; sad; miserable; joyful.*
> *A. shabby (it does not refer to feelings as do all the other four words).*

1. handsome; ugly; beautiful; lazy; lovely.
2. big; large; enormous; tiny; huge.
3. square; round; oblong; oval; tall.
4. larger; biggest; taller; smaller; worse.
5. his; ours; her; your; my.
6. young; healthy; modern; ancient; old.
7. many; twenty; several; few; some.
8. blue; light; black; red; orange.
9. seven; seventeen; seventy; seventy-five; seventh.
10. this; that; these; theirs; those.

Question 4. Here are ten sentences. The two halves of each sentence have been misplaced. Put them together correctly.

1. As soon as the rain stops —— because it was too heavy for him.
2. Put your things away —— the more mistakes you will make.
3. He worked away —— as carefully as you did last term.
4. If I had a lot of money —— he doesn't earn much money.
5. He whispered to me —— we'll go to the cinema.
6. The gazelle ran so fast —— so that nobody else should hear.
7. The more you hurry —— as if his life depended on it.
8. Although he works hard —— I would travel all over the world.

9. You are not doing your work —— that it was soon out of sight.

10. He had to drop his end of the box —— where you can find them.

Question 5. Explain in your own words the meaning of the phrases in bold type in the following sentences:

1. The doctor will be here **within half an hour.**
2. Most of Shakespeare's poetry is **above criticism.**
3. Zanzibar is an island **off the coast of** East Africa.
4. That **goes without saying.**
5. I've got nothing to read. I've **left** my novel **behind.**
6. It's a pity to spoil good work **for want of** a little more care.
7. Many people are **out of work** at the present time.
8. You're nearest to the radio. Let's hear **what's on.**
9. I **was under the impression that** he was worried about something.
10. That's **beyond a joke.**

Question 6

A. Here are some sentences in old-fashioned English. Re-write them using the modern English form.

1. Touch me not!
2. Come you from Padua?
3. I believe it not.
4. Think you he will come?
5. Knew you not Caesar?

B. Correct these sentences:

1. Do you have any sisters?
2. I hadn't my breakfast early this morning.
3. After he seen his teacher he went home.

4. Tom went to the seaside last holidays and so went I.

5. Why didn't you your homework last night?

Question 7.   In each of the following sentences there are two gaps.   Choose suitable words from this list to fill the gaps correctly:

> Either —— or;   As —— so;   such —— that;
> If —— then;   both —— and;   No sooner —— than;
> so —— that;   Whether —— or;   The —— the;
> Neither —— nor.

1. —— my brother —— my sister is old enough to go to school yet.
2. —— had I settled down to read —— the telephone rang.
3. —— you stand out in the rain, —— of course you'll catch cold.
4. —— you come with me —— not, I want to go to the concert.
5. The lightning was —— vivid —— I could see every blade of grass.
6. It was —— an amusing book —— I laughed till I cried.
7. —— older you grow, —— more tolerant you should be.
8. —— you sow, —— shall you reap.
9. —— you haven't been listening —— you are being deliberately stupid.
10. A statement cannot at the same time be —— true —— false.

Question 8.   Complete the following:

1. Two is to second as one is to ——.
2. Second is to —— as minute is to hour.
3. Clever is to cleverness as stupid is to ——.
4. This is to these as —— is to those.

F

5. —— is to rain as parasol is to sun.
6. Sailor is to —— as soldier is to army.
7. Shilling is to pound as hundredweight is to ——.
8. Had been is to was as —— is to took.
9. Hexagon is to triangle as —— is to three.
10. Thither is to whither as thence is to ——.

Question 9. The following list of words consists of ten pairs.
Both words in each pair have a similar meaning. Pair the
words correctly:

afraid;	empty;	enormous;	enough;
feeble;	frightened;	happy;	huge;
joyful;	lofty;	odd;	squirm;
stern;	strange;	strict;	sufficient;
tall;	vacant;	weak;	wriggle.

Question 10. In each of the following lines of five words there
is one which is out of place. Find it and give a group-name
to the four words you have left.
    Example:
        Q. Orange; banana; apple; onion; plum.
        A. a. onion   b. Fruits.

1. Peter; Charles; James; Mary; Henry.
2. Two; four; six; seven; eight.
3. Grasshopper; bee; locust; wasp; worm.
4. Cricket; soccer; chess; hockey; rugby.
5. London; Paris; Madrid; Sweden; Berlin.
6. Wine; beer; water; steam; vinegar.
7. Violin; piano; concert; guitar; flute.
8. Spear; club; sword; dagger; bayonet.
9. Canoe; dhow; caravan; liner; yacht.
10. Diamond; ruby; sapphire; platinum; emerald.

ANSWERS

TEST-PAPER IV

Answer 1

A. 1. He knew he had made a mistake.
   2. They wanted to be paid early on Saturday.
   3. He thought he was going to pass.
   4. We were sure that it would rain.
   5. I always did what I thought was right.

B. Introductory 'that' may be inserted after the reporting verb.

   1. She said she was going home soon.
   2. She said the carpenter could mend it.
   3. He said (told me) he would always remember me.
   4. He said a thief had stolen his purse a few minutes before.
   5. I said (told her) I wanted to see what she had done.

Answer 2

CLOTHING	ANIMALS	METALS	VEGETABLES	BIRDS
belt	camel	gold	cabbage	crow
blouse	gazelle	iron	onion	kite
jacket	giraffe	lead	potato	ostrich
tie	puppy	silver	turnip	pigeon

Answer 3

Egyptian	Spanish
Ireland	Holland
Italian	Congolese
Poland	Japan
Portuguese	Ghanaian

Answer 4

1. anxiously	6. hard
2. fast	7. possibly
3. foolishly	8. respectfully
4. well	9. wholly
5. merrily	10. late

Answer 5

1. married to	6. congratulated our school on
2. good at	7. sound different on
3. staring at	8. interested in
4. satisfied with	9. too busy to do
5. left for	10. Ask him

Answer 6

1. One untrue	6. Possible
2. Possible	7. One untrue
3. One untrue	8. Possible
4. Possible	9. One untrue
5. Possible	10. Possible

Answer 7

1. so	3. but
2. but	4. or

5. although
6. but
7. and

8. but
9. because
10. so

Answer 8

1. March
2. horse
3. true
4. foot
5. men's

6. vegetable
7. sour
8. sheep
9. duke
10. mice

Answer 9

1. Was she very clever?
2. Is he leaving for London tonight?
3. Can't pigs fly?
4. Does Tom do his work well?
5. Did he do up his shoe-lace?
6. Did his parents buy a large house?
7. Does his mother give him pocket-money every week?
8. Must we be kind to others?
9. Did he steal any apples?
10. Is what you've just said true?

Answer 10

1. wrapped
2. Although
3. descendant
4. Principal
5. dessert

6. marvellous
7. thief
8. their
9. sowing
10. column

TEST-PAPER V

Answer 1

1. After he had done his work he went to bed.
2. Last night I saw a very good film.
3. I have been working hard since two o'clock.
4. If you boil water it turns into steam.
5. You ought not to do that.
6. If it rains tomorrow, the match will be cancelled.
7. He wants to be a doctor.
8. Every one of these mangoes is rotten.
9. Last night, while I was doing my homework, the doctor came.
10. I can see five birds out of the window. They are flying very low.

Answer 2

A. 1. uncle
   2. cube
   3. crawl
   4. cow
   5. ruby

B. 1. female relatives
   2. plane figures
   3. noises
   4. young animals
   5. metals

Answer 3

1. disobedient
2. narrow
3. dear
4. scarce
5. ancient

6. shallow
7. senior
8. permanent
9. fertile
10. maximum

Answer 4

1. regularly
2. sensibly
3. shabbily
4. immediately
5. gradually

6. generously
7. punctually
8. courageously
9. dejectedly
10. triumphantly

Answer 5

1. in
2. for
3. on
4. against
5. from

6. between
7. in
8. to
9. on
10. from

Answer 6

A. 1. She was too late to catch the train.
   2. He is too old to work.
   3. He is too proud to visit his former friends.
   4. She was too lazy to sweep under the chairs.
   5. I am too tired to stay up any longer.

B. 1. It is too wet for us to play football.
   2. This sum is too difficult for her to do.
   3. The box is too heavy for you to lift.

4. It was too late for them to get a bus home.
5. He spoke too fast for me to understand what he was saying.

Answer 7

1. He asked me what I would like for my birthday.
2. Cinderella was very unhappy, wasn't she?
3. Mr. Smith taught us how to make paper aeroplanes.
4. Our hens laid four eggs yesterday.
5. Why are you making such a noise?
6. They left their luggage at the station.
7. She lay down on the grass in the warm sunshine.
8. This pair of scissors is not very sharp.
9. Neither of these two books is very interesting.
10. We had a lesson yesterday about Shakespeare who, our teacher said, was the greatest English playwright.

Answer 8

1. Bat
2. no
3. answer
4. yesterday
5. mutton
6. geese
7. letter
8. dirty
9. heard
10. them

Answer 9

1. Peter and I hope to see you again oon.
2. That's not your bag. Whose is it?
3. They amused themselves by playing a new game.
4. May John and I go to the pictures tonight?
5. Look at these two colours and tell me which you prefer.
6. Where is the book which (that) I lent you last week?

7. Father gave my sister and me a shilling each.
8. That dog seems to have hurt its leg.
9. Between you and me, I'm rather worried about it.
10. Last night, I met my uncle from America whom I'd never seen before.

Answer 10

1. **courage**; **courageous**
2. **Italy**; Italian
3. relate; **relative**
4. **artist**; artistic
5. photograph; photographer
6. **regular**; regularity
7. electric; electricity
8. **metal**; metallic
9. **acci**dent; accidental
10. mechanic; **mechanism**

TEST-PAPER VI

Answer 1

1. elongate
2. narrate
3. celebrate
4. hesitate
5. create
6. debate
7. elevate
8. dislocate
9. confiscate
10. dictate

Answer 2

1. aunt
2. men
3. Queen
4. wizard

5. vixen
6. bull
7. niece
8. sir
9. spinster
10. widower
11. tigress
12. son
13. she
14. grandfather
15. mistress
16. male
17. goddess
18. Boy Scout
19. sister-in-law
20. duke

Answer 3

1. of
2. on
3. with
4. of
5. for
6. of
7. for
8. of
9. for
10. with

Answer 4

1. Did you go there yesterday?
2. Foreigners can sometimes write English very well.
3. I have just finished this book.
4. He never goes to bed early.
5. We are going to France for our holidays.
6. We have lost only two matches this season.
7. I must be at the airport by seven o'clock tomorrow morning.
8. Have you ever been here before?
9. I nearly always have toast for breakfast.
10. The First World War ended at 11 a.m. on November 11th 1918.

Answer 5

1. since 9 p.m. last night
2. from 7 p.m. onwards
3. from 6 p.m. to 8 p.m. every evening
4. at 12 p.m. exactly
5. between 4.30 p.m. and 5 p.m.
6. by 7.10 a.m.
7. at about 7.45 p.m.
8. at 8.15 a.m.
9. till 8.35 a.m.
10. at exactly 11.37 p.m.

Answer 6

1. what this means.
2. where the accident occurred/happened.
3. As soon as I reached London,
4. because he is rude.
5. Although he had a bad cold,
6. when the next bus leaves for Manchester.
7. how you make a curry.
8. although he did not work very hard.
9. Because this man was stupid,
10. why you don't want to go.

Answer 7

A. 1. He is such a rich man that he has his own aeroplane.
2. Ireland is such a small country that it would fit inside Lake Victoria.
3. John was such a greedy boy that he took all the sweets.
4. She is such a kind girl that everybody loves her.
5. They went at such a speed that we were left behind.

B. 1. He was so kind that everybody loved him.
   2. Cinderella was so beautiful that the Prince wanted to marry her.
   3. You are so clever that you will pass the examination easily.
   4. My dog is so fierce that we are not afraid of burglars.
   5. Yesterday was so cold that we couldn't have P.E. outside.

Answer 8

1. Dutch
2. tricycle
3. dollar
4. won't
5. Italy
6. a hundred
7. Berlin
8. fortnight
9. thirty
10. spoken

Answer 9

1. very heavily.
2. soundly
3. in good times and in bad.
4. teasing me.
5. very nearly forty years old.
6. very irritating
7. introducing irrelevant points.
8. short of money
9. in your position.
10. into trouble.

Answer 10

1. —— c.
2. —— e.
3. —— h.
4. —— j.
5. —— d.
6. —— b.
7. —— a.
8. —— i.
9. —— f.
10. —— g.

TEST-PAPER VII

Answer 1.   Yesterday after school I came home and did my homework. Then I had my tea. For tea I ate some sandwiches and drank a glass of milk my mother had got ready for me. After tea I went to my father's shop. I sold things to the customers. Whenever they bought anything I wrote down its name and cost. At six o'clock I began to clean the shop. I swept the floor and dusted the shelves. At a quarter to seven it grew dark and my father brought me back home in his van.

Answer 2

A. 1. a flock   2. a swarm   3. a pack   4. a fleet   5. a shoal

Several answers may be acceptable in numbers 6 to 10. Two examples are given for each:

6. grapes; flowers
7. labourers; ruffians
8. horses; cricketers
9. beads; pearls
10. bushes; trees

Answer 3

1. describe	6. satisfied
2. fill	7. endanger
3. obeys	8. decide
4. widened	9. please
5. Heat	10. enjoying

Answer 4.   There are of course numerous ways of completing the sentences.   Here are some suggestions:

1. as soon as the doors were opened.
2. wherever they please.
3. as if I had offended him in some way.
4. because I didn't get to bed till two o'clock.
5. although he has never had music lessons.
6. so that I am sure I get the address correct.
7. such . . . that I became impatient with him.
8. as careful as you used to be.
9. the more I long to go there.
10. unless you work much harder.

Answer 5

1. after
2. down
3. on
4. above
5. outside
6. behind
7. out of
8. away from
9. without
10. including

Answer 6.   The following are *suggestions* for suitable answers:

1. Whenever I go on a long train-journey . . .
2. that I had nothing to do with this letter.
3. since he left India in 1950.
4. Unless I hear from him soon . . .
5. as if he's hurt his foot.
6. to whom I was introduced last night.
7. after you've finished your painting.
8. that money attracts men strongly.
9. As soon as he opened the safe . . .
10. The man whom you insulted . . .

Answer 7.   Here are some examples of *natural* questions:

1. How long do you expect to be away?
2. If you mix red and blue, what colour do you get?
3. When does the mail usually arrive?
4. What is the name of the present queen of England?
5. Exactly how far is it from your house to school?
6. Three times five?
7. Do you think you'll be able to get a Scholarship to the University?
8. When did we last see each other?
9. Which is your favourite subject?
10. Where did you hang my coat, please?

Answer 8

1. last	6. sow
2. aeroplane	7. husband
3. single	8. lower
4. but	9. profitable
5. score	10. put

Answer 9.   'Hello, John!' said Tom.   'I was hoping you'd ring me this morning.   It's a long time since we've seen you. If you're not busy on Thursday, can you and Mary come round about seven o'clock?'

'What a pity!' answered John.   'We'd have liked to come very much.   But Mary's brother, whom you probably remember, has just arrived from Manchester.   We can't very well leave him by himself, can we?'   'That's all right. Bring him along too,' said Tom.   'We'll be very glad to see him.'

Answer 10

1. they
2. stove
3. bead
4. plough
5. quay

6. real
7. town
8. wheat
9. draught
10. forth

TEST-PAPER VIII

Answer 1

1. Mr. M. wanted Mr. S. **to do** the work.
2. Mr. M. ordered Mr. S. **to do** the work.
3. Mr. M. made Mr. S. **do** the work.
4. Mr. M. saw Mr. S. **doing** the work.
5. Mr. M. prevented Mr. S. **from doing** the work.
6. Mr. M. asked Mr. S. **if he had done** (would do) the work.
7. Mr. M. hoped **that** Mr. S. **would do** the work next day.
8. Mr. M. expected Mr. S. **to do** the work.
9. Mr. M. thanked Mr. S. **for doing** (having done) the work.
10. Mr. M. suggested **that** Mr. S. **should do** the work next morning.

Answer 2

1. **two** wheels
2. **under** the sea
3. judge **wrongly**
4. **not** human
5. **before** the war

6. **without** care
7. **full** of beauty
8. **make** simple
9. **female** waiter
10. **able** to be moved

Answer 3

1. enough	6. few
2. many	7. little
3. any	8. All
4. a little	9. several
5. a few	10. most

Answer 4

1. for five years
2. well enough
3. as hard as
4. for a year
5. twice
6. quite true
7. While I was
8. more slowly
9. quite certain
10. The Governor also came to our Open Day. OR The Governor came to our Open Day too.

Answer 5

1. **in** Bombay —— **in** England.
2. to get home **by** bus OR on the bus.
3. the matter **with** you —— pale **to** me.
4. **at** a big desk —— at the front **of** ——.
5. **with** that razor blade ——. Ask Peter ——.
6. **To** my surprise —— **by** herself ——.
7. **at** London Airport —— **in** the afternoon.
8. **through** the window-pane —— **off** the table.
9. **on** this parcel —— **by** surface-mail.
10. different **from** Peter's —— baek **to** your desk ——.

G

Answer 6

1. what he says.
2. what you mean by 'easy'.
3. where the Bank is.
4. that my brother had measles.
5. whether you do it or not.
6. how kind you had been to him.
7. why he ordered three copies of yesterday's paper.
8. who was responsible for the accident.
9. that you won't be able to come to my party.
10. when the examination results will be published.

Answer 7

A. 1. walk
  2. visited
  3. quarrelled
  4. fly
  5. disembarked

B. 1. come/go on bicycles
  2. make longer
  3. make up my mind
  4. make better
  5. said he was sorry

Answer 8

1. peninsula
2. South-West
3. eighteenth
4. export
5. continent
6. giant
7. aquarium
8. dog
9. flowers
10. Twins

Answer 9

1. Pigs are sometimes called swine.
2. passers-by —— lorries.

3. knives —— bread.
4. two spoonfuls —— two spoons full
5. was combing her hair.
6. potatoes —— loaves
7. calves —— cats
8. monkeys —— roofs
9. trousers —— scissors.
10. sheep —— brothers-in-law.

Answer 10

A. 1. 'I am sorry that I haven't been able to come before.'
   2. 'Have you (got) your driving-licence on you, (sir)?'
   3. 'May we go for a picnic, Mother?'
   4. 'I haven't had time to ice the cake for your birthday.'
   5. 'I shall have to stay at home tomorrow.'

B. 1. My uncle asked me if I knew why zebras are striped.
   2. My grandmother told my sister Mary that she wanted her to stay with her for the holidays.
   3. My mother told me to be careful not to miss my bus.
   4. The workman said that he would try to do it as soon as he had time.
   5. Mr. Smith asked his wife if his suit had been sent to the cleaners.

TEST-PAPER IX

Answer 1

1. limped
2. shrieked

3. drifting
4. mumbled

5. wriggled
6. retorted
7. curled

8. agreed
9. glided
10. pleaded

Answer 2

A. 1. a greengrocer
   2. a caretaker
   3. a butcher
   4. a conductor
   5. a reporter

B. 1. a man who looks after a flock of sheep.
   2. a man who makes clothes.
   3. a woman who looks after sick people.
   4. a man who designs buildings.
   5. a man who makes things with iron.

Answer 3

1. endless
2. wonderful
3. dangerous
4. greenish
5. friendly

6. magnetic
7. eatable
8. conversational
9. expressive
10. secondary

Answer 4

1. resolved
2. reproved
3. dissolved
4. strode
5. approached

6. resented
7. prescribed
8. implored
9. muttered
10. strolled

Answer 5

1. for	6. between
2. of	7. at
3. in	8. into
4. by	9. for
5. around	10. over

Answer 6

A.		B.	
	1. I don't know.		1. freezes
	2. No.		2. had listened
	3. I don't know.		3. had
	4. Yes.		4. would not have done
	5. No.		5. will be able

Answer 7.   (Suggested answers.)

1. He says it is impossible for him to come.
2. Your writing is illegible.
3. The mountain was (clearly) visible.
4. It has not rained at all for several days.
5. John goes to the cinema every week.
6. According to the magistrate, the prisoner was innocent.
7. He was quite certain he would pass the examination.
8. I have read many of Shaw's plays.
9. None of these apples is green.
10. Livingstone is a very famous explorer.

Answer 8

1. well	6. depth
2. time	7. spoken
3. lengthen	8. often (frequently)
4. Second	9. do
5. Thursday	10. better

Answer 9

1. the youngest boy	6. an article
2. an exercise	7. a more generous man
3. studying Mathematics	8. the more difficult
4. a handkerchief	9. the shortest distance
5. the centre	10. Humility

Answer 10

A. 1. We shall not
   2. She will not
   3. He used not
   4. Am I not
   5. Do you not

B. 1. I didn't see him yesterday.
   2. Don't do that!
   3. He doesn't like reading.
   4. She won't be able to come.
   5. He didn't know what to do.

TEST-PAPER X

Answer 1

A. 1. Had he enough money?
   2. Will she be able to come?
   3. Did you do your homework last night?
   4. Do they know how to do it?
   5. Can we get there before six?

B. 1. Doesn't he know the answer?
   2. Didn't he know the answer?
   3. Didn't the train leave punctually?

4. Didn't she see him last night?

5. Didn't he put the money in his pocket?

Answer 2.   Suggestions for simple answers are:

1. A kangaroo has a long muscular **tail.**
   A **tale** is very much the same as a story.
2. Bread is made of **flour** and water and yeast.
   Usually the **flower** of a plant appears before the fruit.
3. During the storm a large **bough** fell from the tree.
   When the Queen comes into a room, all the men **bow.**
4. There were twenty years of **peace** between the two world wars.
   Would you like another **piece** of cake?
5. Last year his business made a large **profit.**
   Sometimes a **prophet** can see into the future.

Answer 3

1. Can you see the big black dog?
2. There were four tiny blue flowers on each stem.
3. The teacher drew a long thin yellow line on the black-board.
4. He is the taller of the two.
5. I am pleased that you can come.
6. Are you tired after all this work?
7. She grew more and more beautiful as the years went on.
8. I found 'Kidnapped' a most exciting story.
9. In times like the present men are anxious about the future.
10. Shakespeare was the greatest playwright of all time.

Answer 4

<table>
<tr><td>1. Possible</td><td>6. Possible</td></tr>
<tr><td>2. One untrue</td><td>7. Possible</td></tr>
<tr><td>3. One untrue</td><td>8. Possible</td></tr>
<tr><td>4. One untrue</td><td>9. One untrue</td></tr>
<tr><td>5. Possible</td><td>10. Possible</td></tr>
</table>

Answer 5

<table>
<tr><td>1. give you a place to sleep</td><td>6. tolerate</td></tr>
<tr><td>2. saved</td><td>7. resemble</td></tr>
<tr><td>3. waiting eagerly for</td><td>8. Write down</td></tr>
<tr><td>4. respect</td><td>9. take up as a hobby
(or business)</td></tr>
<tr><td>5. postponing</td><td>10. consider</td></tr>
</table>

Answer 6

A. 1. on his visits to the Game Park.
   2. In spite of frequent interruptions . . .
   3. Immediately after his arrival at his brother's house . . .
   4. To my great surprise . . .
   5. Because of the serious injury to his leg . . .

B. 1. Although he tried very hard . . .
   2. When he received this information . . .
   3. Before aeroplanes were invented . . .
   4. Because he was poor . . .
   5. Whenever they could . . .

Answer 7

A. 1. stubborn
   2. proud
   3. blind
   4. brave
   5. busy

B. 1. a rock
   2. ice
   3. a needle (a razor)
   4. a feather
   5. snow

Answer 8

1. reddish	6. whom
2. breadth	7. here
3. boys'	8. glove
4. ours	9. where
5. wrote	10. beginning

Answer 9

1. Who	6. When
2. Which	7. How much
3. Where	8. How many
4. What	9. How often
5. Why	10. How

Answer 10

always	convenient
parallel	skilful
ceiling	disappointed
garage	medicine
separate	vaccinate

TEST-PAPER XI

Answer 1

1. seen	6. done
2. struck	7. fed
3. eaten	8. drunk
4. written	9. bought
5. sung	10. gone

Answer 2

1. a. **ex**ports
   b. **export**
2. a. con**tent**
   b. **contents**
3. a. **record**
   b. re**cord**

4. a. ob**ject**
   b. **object**
5. a. **progress**
   b. pro**gress**

Answer 3

1. satisfactory
2. grateful
3. enjoyable
4. Disobedient
5. poisonous

6. amusing
7. momentary
8. advisable
9. skilful
10. Careless

Answer 4

1. busily
2. bravely
3. during the week
4. everywhere
5. visibly

6. an hour ago
7. besides
8. always
9. in March
10. immediately

Answer 5

1. a. While he was in the cellar he poured some beer.
   b. He was outside the cellar and poured beer into it.
2. a. The rabbit ran from one side to the other.
   b. It ran up or down the middle of the road.
3. a. He took a picture of the counter with his camera.
   b. He removed a photograph from the counter.
4. a. Livingstone gave the money in exchange for the slave.
   b. He made a present of the money to the slave.
5. a. As a result of your suggestion, I will do this.
   b. Although you may not approve, I intend to do this.

Answer 6

1. An auctioneer is a man who sells things to the highest bidder at a public sale.
2. An author is a man who writes books.
3. A bachelor is a man who has never married.
4. A burglar is a man who breaks into a building at night, to steal.
5. A chauffeur is a man who drives and looks after a private motor-car.
6. A hermit is a person who lives alone usually in order to lead a holy life.
7. A pauper is a person who has no income, money or property.
8. A sculptor is a man who shapes things (especially statues) out of clay, wood, stone, etc.
9. A teetotaller is a person who does not take strong drink.
10. A warder is a man who guards prisoners.

Answer 7

1. wasn't he?
2. can you?
3. don't you?
4. has he?
5. won't you?
6. didn't he?
7. will you?
8. mustn't they?
9. is it?
10. has he?

Answer 8

1. sight
2. noun
3. worst
4. cube
5. Cub
6. bow
7. dark
8. fins
9. a sixth
10. shall

Answer 9

A.

I	me	my	mine
You	you	your	yours
He	him	his	his
She	her	her	hers
We	us	our	ours
They	them	their	theirs

B. 1. we
2. us
3. you
4. our
5. theirs

Answer 10

a. ——————— 8   f. ——————— 9
b. ——————— 5   g. ——————— 2
c. ——————— 3   h. ——————— 6
d. ——————— 1   i. ——————— 7
e. ——————— 4   j. ——————— 10

TEST-PAPER XII

Answer 1

1. ticks
2. peal
3. rustled
4. pattering
5. banging
6. crackled
7. creak
8. beating/beat
9. howling
10. screeched

Answer 2

Books	boxes	toys	flies
monkeys	babies	women	children
hands	feet	teeth	spoonfuls
sheep	thieves	knives	halves
roofs	potatoes	houses	mice

Answer 3

1. lazy
2. tiny
3. tall
4. biggest
5. ours
6. healthy
7. twenty
8. light
9. seventh
10. theirs

Answer 4

1. As soon as the rain stops we'll go to the cinema.
2. Put your things away where you can find them.
3. He worked away as if his life depended on it.
4. If I had a lot of money I would travel all over the world.
5. He whispered to me so that nobody else should hear.
6. The gazelle ran so fast that it was soon out of sight.

7. The more you hurry the more mistakes you will make.
8. Although he works hard he doesn't earn much money.
9. You are not doing your work as carefully as you did last term.
10. He had to drop his end of the box because it was too heavy for him.

Answer 5.   The following suggestions explain the meanings as simply as possible:

1. before half an hour has passed.
2. too good to be criticised.
3. near to the coast of . . .
4. That is too obvious to need any explanation.
5. I've not brought my novel with me.
6. because (you) have not been careful enough.
7. unemployed . . .
8. the programme.
9. I had the idea that (I thought that) . . .
10. too serious (annoying) to be amusing.

Answer 6

A. 1. Don't (Do not) touch me!
   2. Do you come from Padua?
   3. I don't (do not) believe it.
   4. Do you think he will come?
   5. Didn't you know (Did you not know) Caesar?

B. 1. Have you any sisters?
   2. I didn't (did not) have my breakfast early this morning.
   3. After he had seen his teacher he went home.
   4. Tom went to the seaside last holidays and so did I.
   5. Why didn't you do (did you not do) your homework last night?

Answer 7

1. Neither my brother nor my sister is old enough to go to school yet.
2. No sooner had I settled down to read than the telephone rang.
3. If you stand out in the rain, then of course you'll catch cold.
4. Whether you come with me or not, I want to go to the concert tonight.
5. The lightning was so vivid that I could see every blade of grass.
6. It was such an amusing book that I laughed till I cried.
7. The older you grow, the more tolerant you should be.
8. As you sow so shall you reap.
9. Either you haven't been listening or you are being deliberately stupid.
10. A statement cannot at the same time be both true and false.

Answer 8

1. first.
2. minute
3. stupidity.
4. that
5. Umbrella
6. navy
7. ton.
8. had taken
9. six
10. whence.

Answer 9

1. afraid; frightened
2. empty; vacant
3. enormous; huge
4. enough; sufficient
5. feeble; weak
6. happy; joyful
7. lofty; tall
8. odd; strange
9. squirm; wriggle
10. stern; strict

Answer 10

1. a. Mary   b. Boys' names.
2. a. Seven   b. Even numbers.
3. a. worm   b. (Flying) insects
4. a. chess   b. Outdoor sports
5. a. Sweden   b. Capitals
6. a. stream   b. Liquids
7. a. concert   b. Musical instruments.
8. a. club   b. Weapons with a pointed blade.
9. a. caravan   b. Ships or boats.
10. a. platinum   b. Precious stones.

PRINTED IN GREAT BRITAIN BY ROBERT MACLEHOSE AND CO. LTD
THE UNIVERSITY PRESS, GLASGOW